Thieves & Kings

ISBN: 0-9681025-1-4

Printed in Canada.

I Box Publishing welcomes any comments or questions at the above address, and may publish/answer them in the letters pages of the on-going comic book series, available at finer comic shops everywhere.

First printing 1997
Second printing 1999

The Millbrook Strips.

Quinton Zempfester took form several years before any of the other characters in the realm of Asaria. His true origins date back much further to stories I penned out in early high-school, and before that, as characters for role playing adventures I never actually got around to playing. (I always found those early role playing games somewhat restrictive. Quinton was not the sort of character who was meant to stalk through dungeons in search of blood and treasure).

Shortly after high-school and my brief stint in art college, it occurred to me that rather than hold down a regular job, I might instead look for something better suiting my artistic pretensions. Something like, I don't know. . . a part time job doing comics? (How could such a thing be done!? Was it possible?) Well, to my young and unjaded mind, the cartoon strips in newspapers looked like just that. They appeared easy enough to do, much less work than doing whole comic pages, and there certainly seemed to be enough money in it if you gained some notoriety. So I decided that I would come up with a series of humour strips and sell them to a big newsprint syndicate. The money, I reasoned, would happily supplement my *Thieves & Kings* bank account, (the cash I was saving up to eventually launch *I Box Publishing)*, and heaven knew I could use the drawing practice.

So, congratulating myself on clever problem solving, I scribbled out a set of strips. (These strips, incidentally, were *not* the Quinton strips printed here, but another series which documented the trials and affairs of a young character who was kicked out of his basement by overwrought parents sick with his lack of direction in life and general loafing about.) These strips drew upon my own experiences as a young man as well as those of the other late teens about me who had grown up in the seventies. (Not that any of us were ever actually kicked out of our homes, mind you, but I think most of us *have* been threatened with the prospect at one time or another.)

When I look at those strips now they still make me laugh, but at the time I judged them unsatisfactory; too distant from my first love. I had also learned that making funny cartoon strips was by no means the quick money scam I originally estimated it to be. If I was going to spend time toiling on such a project, I thought it would be better to do something which might augment and enhance my work on *Thieves & Kings*. Kill two birds with one stone, and all that.

So I started over.

Once again I congratulated myself on bright problem solving, and drew up another mess of strips, this time concerning Quinton Zempfester. I picked one of my favourite points in his history, which dealt with his summer at the Jay household in Millbrook, and went from there. After several long weeks of fevered drawing, I packaged up about thirty of the better strips into three identical presentation folders and took a trip into the city.

Now, this was another part of my ingenious plan. (I knew alarmingly little about publishing at this point. I was doomed to learn). Rather than mail my submissions into the various newspapers and have them land on mountainous slush piles ('slush pile' being the publisher's term for 'unopened submissions'), I would instead go down and gain an audience with the editors in person.

To this end, I arrived at the three major newspapers in Toronto and called up to the comic strip editor's desk from the courtesy phones in the lobbies. I would ask how to submit material, and after listening politely, would then say, 'Oh, well actually, I'm in your lobby right now. Perhaps I could come up and show you my work?'

The editors of newspaper comic strip sections don't ever want to see an artist in person. Rejection is much easier to do anonymously. So hopefully, my tactic would increase my chances of clinching a contract.

The *Toronto Star*, (the big left wing paper), saw through my little scheme immediately, and though they allowed me to bring up my submission in person, they filed it on top of their slush pile while I watched, and then told me not to call them, they'd call me. I received their rejection letter a few weeks later. Crash.

Next was the *Toronto Sun*, (the right wing paper for angry racists with a pin-up girl on page two). Their editor was completely caught off guard. He tried to tell me to go away and mail the thing in. I told him this was silly, and that not to worry, it'd just take a moment to pop up and hand it to him. When I found my way to his office, his desk was empty. Coffee was still sloshing in his cup and a half smoked cigarette was still smoldering in the ash tray. I waited around until the cigarette stopped smoking, and then left, leaving my package on his desk. I was afraid that I'd come on way too strong with this fellow, and that he'd reject me on principle. Indeed, he mailed out his rejection notice the very next day. Though, he surprised me by being very polite in his letter, taking the time to suggest a career in children's literature. How nice. Crash number two.

The Globe & Mail, (the big right wing paper for wealthy business people, and what I felt was the least likely of the lot to give me the time of day), shocked me by giving the most welcoming response of all. The comics page editor was out that day, so the editor in chief of the whole darn newspaper picked up the phone and listened to my pitch. When I told him I was in the lobby, he said, 'Really? Wow! I'll be right down!'

He came down to the lobby and shook my hand and took me up to a big office where we talked about comics and publishing for half an hour. He promised to pass my work on to the comics editor the next morning, which he did. The comics page editor then called me in person to reject Quinton. Very classy. Still, this was crash number three and I was back at square one.

In the end, two things had become obvious. The first was that a daily comic strip was a full time job. You had to come up with consistently good material and creative drawings every day. How I would be able to manage that and produce pages of *Thieves & Kings* was a question I wasn't willing to answer. And the second thing was that I discovered the comic strip market was so incredibly competitive that the chances of getting picked up were virtually nil. Particularly since my work was clearly amateurish and rather unconventional, —the *Toronto Star* editor added in his letter that 'this was a laugh-a-day world we lived in, and that on-going stories were a thing of the past.' Oh well.

So I wound up getting a regular job like everybody else. I sold lottery tickets for a year or two, and repaired lawn mowers for another. Among other things.

Anyway, the upshot of all this was that I wound up with this extra background material. So, way back in issue number two, I picked out a small assortment of the better Quinton strips and printed them. I chose not to reprint them in the first collected volume, thinking that they would be much better suited in this one where the Quinton-Heath story line really gets going.

And so, ladies and gentlemen, I present *Quinton Zempfester, Madman of Millbrook.*

The Millbrook Strips.

WHY AREN'T YOU EATING, QUINTON? I THOUGHT YOU WERE HUNGRY.

DO NOT MISTAKE MY ACTIONS, MRS. JAY. I DO NOT MEAN TO INSULT YOUR FINE COOKING.

I JUST DON'T WANT TO EAT ANYTHING THAT MIGHT KILL ME.

PARDON ME?

POISON, I MEAN! —I'D BETTER CHECK THE BASEMENT FOR ASSASSINS TOO. EXCUSE ME.

WELL, WE HAVE CERTAINLY HAD LESS INTERESTING GUESTS...

HOW LONG DID YOU SAY HE'S STAYING?

MOM, WHAT IF THE COUNCIL DID SEND QUINTON HERE TO PROTECT HIM FROM ASSASSINS, AND NOT BECAUSE HE'S CRAZY?

DAVIN, YOU MUSTN'T SAY TO QUINTON THAT HE'S CRAZY. IT WOULDN'T BE NICE.

BUT WHAT IF HE'S NOT?

OH HONEY, IF THERE WERE ASSASSINS ABOUT, WE'D JUST HAVE TO DO OUR BEST TO PROTECT THE FAMILY. NOW GOODNIGHT.

DID YOU HEAR THAT?!

YEAH! —BOY, IT'LL SURE BE EASIER WITH SOMEONE TO HELP ME! C'MON, WE'LL CLIMB OUT THE WINDOW!

WHAT DO WE DO WHEN WE FIND AN ASSASSIN?

WE CLUB HIM, TIE HIM UP, AND THEN FIND OUT WHO SENT HIM.

WHAT IF HE WON'T TELL US?

DON'T WORRY. —HE'LL BE SO ALARMED WITH THE EASE AND SKILL WITH WHICH WE CATCH HIM, HE'LL BE SURE TO SPILL HIS GUTS! —PASS ME THE CLUB.

WE DIDN'T BRING ONE.

When We Last Left Our Hero. . .

Welcome to the second volume of *Thieves & Kings*.

I'm glad you could make it.

If you are new to the story, or a bit rusty on details read long enough ago to have perhaps forgotten, here's a quick recap:

—The story began with a boy named Rubel, who's birth was surrounded by magic and mystery. Brought up by his grandfather and by a wizard named Quinton, Rubel, believing in magic, decided to become a thief. A *noble* thief.

One day when he was ten, he met in the woods the princess of the realm. She was eleven. Her name was Katara, and she was caught in a problem beyond her solving. Through a stroke of luck and mischief, the young thief managed to right her dilemma and in doing so, foiled the plans of her evil older brother and a wicked witch, both of whom had designs upon the throne of Asaria. This done, Rubel swore himself to the princess, and she to him. Shortly afterwards, Rubel went off to travel the world with his Grandfather.

Upon his return four years later, Rubel found that all his friends had vanished. His Grandfather was dead, the princess had gone missing under questionable circumstances, and Rubel was confronted by the sorceress, Soracia; the *Shadow Lady*.

The Shadow Lady wove black magic about Rubel and tried to steal his soul. She would have succeeded but for Rubel's oldest friend, little Varkias the imp. With the aid of the Angel's Tree, Varkias came to Rubel's rescue at the last moment, and together they escaped Soracia.

The very next day she cast another spell in a second bid to capture his soul, but again failed. In that second failure, however, the Queen of Halves planted the seeds for her third and final attempt. . .

Chapter 1

Oh girls and ladies my belief
'Tis three a chance to catch a thief,
And thieves cannot be caught by trickery.

But have thee luck and pure heart,
The noble thief's a noble art
For then three wishes will he grant to thee!

See over rooftop, yonder slopes
A-running quick and yarning hopes
Pause every hand to rest for now their chore.

With rusty sword and broken crown
The king of thieves has come to town
To dance in song thy glory gone to war!

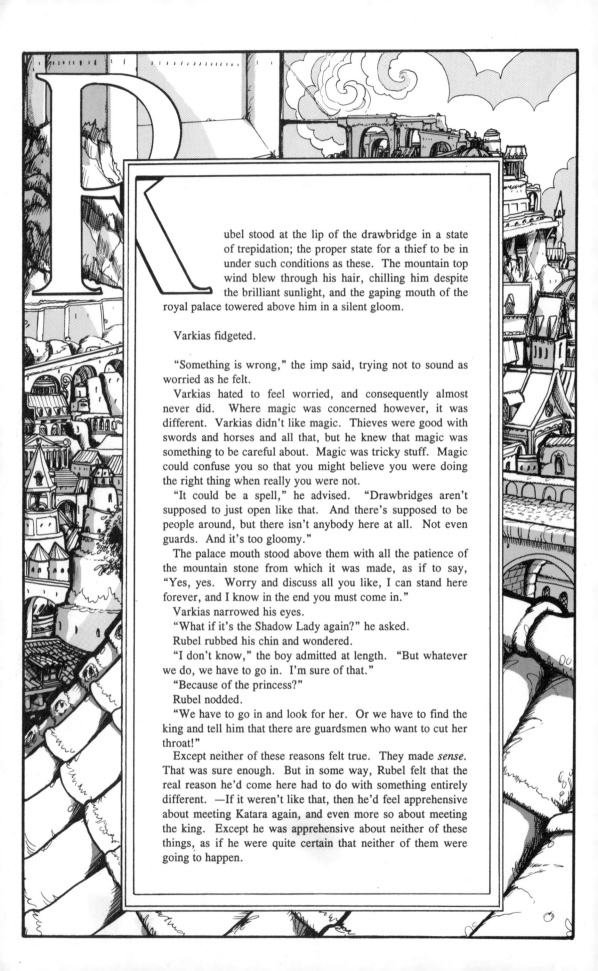

ubel stood at the lip of the drawbridge in a state of trepidation; the proper state for a thief to be in under such conditions as these. The mountain top wind blew through his hair, chilling him despite the brilliant sunlight, and the gaping mouth of the royal palace towered above him in a silent gloom.

Varkias fidgeted.

"Something is wrong," the imp said, trying not to sound as worried as he felt.

Varkias hated to feel worried, and consequently almost never did. Where magic was concerned however, it was different. Varkias didn't like magic. Thieves were good with swords and horses and all that, but he knew that magic was something to be careful about. Magic was tricky stuff. Magic could confuse you so that you might believe you were doing the right thing when really you were not.

"It could be a spell," he advised. "Drawbridges aren't supposed to just open like that. And there's supposed to be people around, but there isn't anybody here at all. Not even guards. And it's too gloomy."

The palace mouth stood above them with all the patience of the mountain stone from which it was made, as if to say, "Yes, yes. Worry and discuss all you like, I can stand here forever, and I know in the end you must come in."

Varkias narrowed his eyes.

"What if it's the Shadow Lady again?" he asked.

Rubel rubbed his chin and wondered.

"I don't know," the boy admitted at length. "But whatever we do, we have to go in. I'm sure of that."

"Because of the princess?"

Rubel nodded.

"We have to go in and look for her. Or we have to find the king and tell him that there are guardsmen who want to cut her throat!"

Except neither of these reasons felt true. They made *sense*. That was sure enough. But in some way, Rubel felt that the real reason he'd come here had to do with something entirely different. —If it weren't like that, then he'd feel apprehensive about meeting Katara again, and even more so about meeting the king. Except he was apprehensive about neither of these things, as if he were quite certain that neither of them were going to happen.

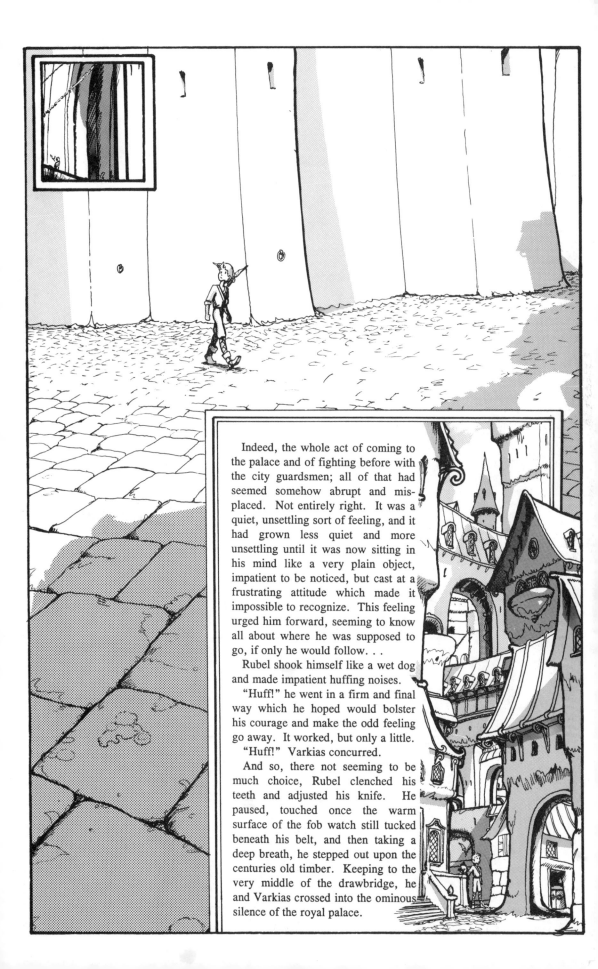

Indeed, the whole act of coming to the palace and of fighting before with the city guardsmen; all of that had seemed somehow abrupt and misplaced. Not entirely right. It was a quiet, unsettling sort of feeling, and it had grown less quiet and more unsettling until it was now sitting in his mind like a very plain object, impatient to be noticed, but cast at a frustrating attitude which made it impossible to recognize. This feeling urged him forward, seeming to know all about where he was supposed to go, if only he would follow. . .

Rubel shook himself like a wet dog and made impatient huffing noises.

"Huff!" he went in a firm and final way which he hoped would bolster his courage and make the odd feeling go away. It worked, but only a little.

"Huff!" Varkias concurred.

And so, there not seeming to be much choice, Rubel clenched his teeth and adjusted his knife. He paused, touched once the warm surface of the fob watch still tucked beneath his belt, and then taking a deep breath, he stepped out upon the centuries old timber. Keeping to the very middle of the drawbridge, he and Varkias crossed into the ominous silence of the royal palace.

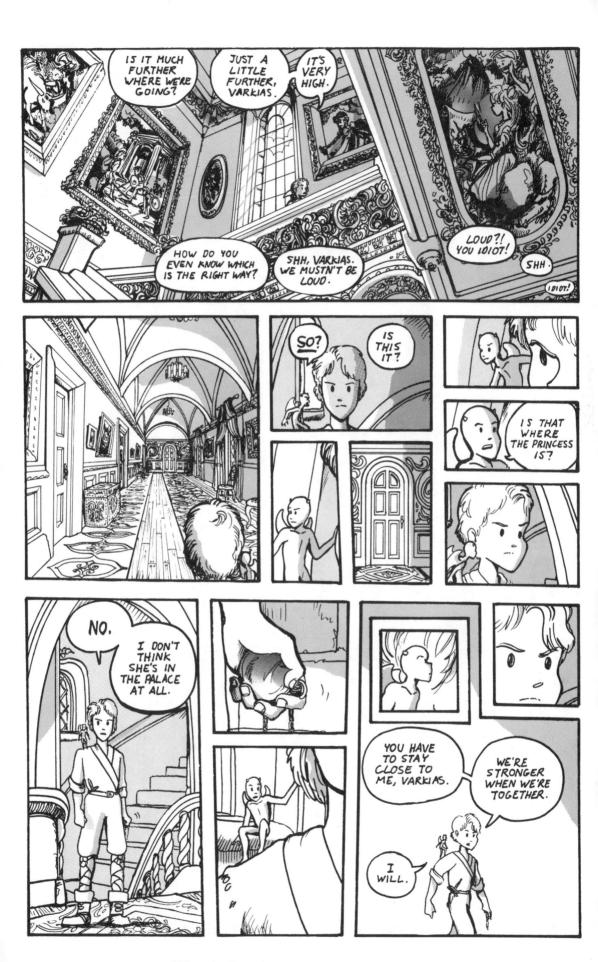

IT'S THE KING!

WOW. HE DOESN'T LOOK SO GOOD.

I THINK HE'S SICK.

HHHHHH.

HHHHHH.

DO YOU THINK WE SHOULD WAKE HIM UP?

MAYBE HE KNOWS WHAT'S GOING ON.

HE DOES BUT YOU CAN'T.

WHA-?

GAK!

AAAARRRRGG!

SLAM!

VARKIAS!

GRRR!

"He runs barefoot across the country side, his eyes set forward with happy intent," she told him in such a matter of fact way that Rubel was caught entirely by surprise and so listened to her with his full attention. "Toward a beach and across the sands which are hot to his skin, but not enough to burn like the sun above which shines upon the shafts of mountain grass," she continued.

Rubel was surprised enough as it was, both by her presence, and by the brilliant hazy way the light had gone in the king's chamber. There seemed almost to be a mirage of trees and grassy hillocks dancing just beyond his vision, he could swear it, but he could not turn to look because his eyes were held by hers.

And the Shadow Lady's words continued to confuse him, which was of course the whole point, though he only realized it after listening for several moments more.

'She is trying to confuse me!' he realized with a gasp. But even then, Rubel found himself involuntarily paying close attention to her peculiar narrative in an effort to sort out what she was saying. Though by the time he had just about done so, the story changed again, confusing him further and making him pay even closer attention. As he tried to concentrate, the Shadow Lady only smiled and her elusive words danced away from him so that he had to chase again in order to catch up. What little thinking Rubel managed above this mesmerizing exercise, ran like this:

'*Arrgh!* This is bad!' he thought, 'And strange! For her to be speaking to me in such a cheerful way. . . Her eyes are not burning into mine as they were yesterday. . . And why is she telling me this story at all? And what is she talking about now, for the story has changed again, and I must listen carefully if I want to catch up. But that is surely what she wants! —To confuse me with her words. She is casting a spell on me! I am sure of it! But how can I stop her? I have the silver watch in my hand with Katara's lock of hair inside. That will protect me. I can swing it at her if she tries anything! Except she is trying something now, she is casting a spell. .! And I am listening, so perhaps it is already cast. ., and what is she saying now? No! I must not listen. Except I already am. . .'

And so forth.

In the end, the struggle to make sense of it all caused Rubel's thinking to become so taxed and confused that the effort of trying to think at all began to seem altogether too much bother. Thus, without another thought, Rubel glided entirely beneath the Shadow Lady's influence, letting the story take him where it would.

It was then that it started to say things to him directly.

"Take this Rubel, and put it on," she said, holding out something to him. "Take the other one off first."
He did.
The thing she handed to him was his old shirt. The one he'd gotten rid of because it had been stained with captain McGovern's blood. Except, he was told, it wasn't really captain McGovern's blood at all. It was *his* blood; from where he had been struck at point blank by the captain's personal gun. —A fact he marveled at for having so easily overlooked. . .

And so, with a gasp of pain, Rubel was shocked back into full awareness. The hazy light flashed out as he collapsed to the floor.

OH, THAT'S AWFULLY PAINFULL...

CAN YOU MOVE ABOUT?

GROWL!!

NO?

YOU MUSTN'T TRY.

YOU'LL HURT YOURSELF VERY BADDLY INSIDE IF YOU DO.

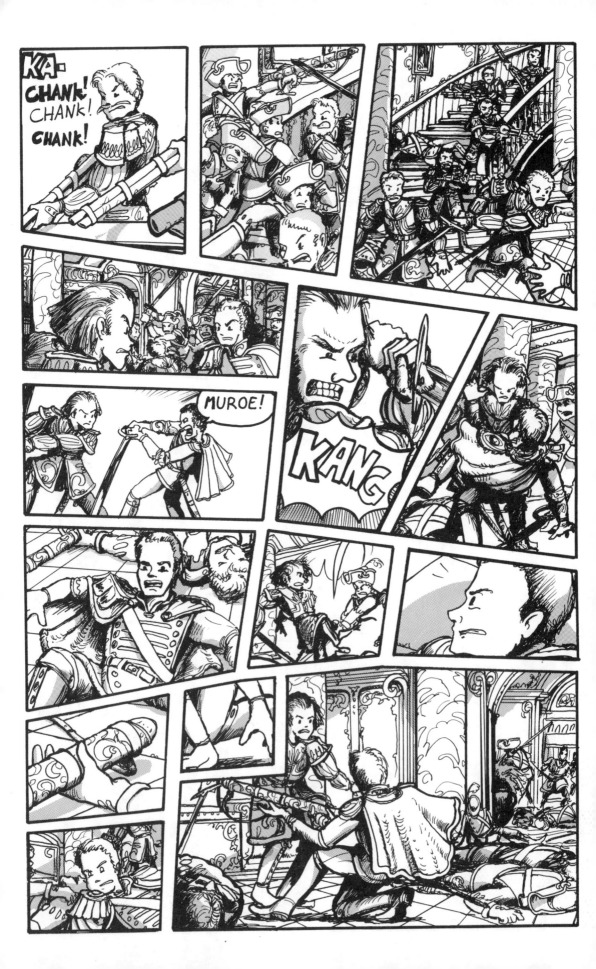

CHAN**SHLUCK**

AWWWGH!

CAPTAIN! WE'VE SECURED THE HALL!

WE ARE ADVANCING ON THEM! —THEY ARE IN A RETREAT!

MUROE MUROE..!

IT'S TOO LATE FOR YOU... YOU WIN **NOTHING** BY THIS!

NOTHING

GOOD! WE MUST NOT GIVE THEM THE CHANCE TO TURN AND FORM A REARGUARD.

WE MUST KEEP THEM IN DISARRAY!

YES SIR!

SIR..!

DON'T YOU FEAR PERHAPS WE HAVE ACTED TOO HASTILY IN THIS?

NO! WE MUST TAKE THE PALACE! WE HAVE WAITED FAR TOO LONG ALREADY! —THE DAMAGE WE HAVE ALLOWED..!

THE PRINCE HAS NO SEASONED WARRIORS.

WE SHALL TAKE THEM BY STORM AND DRIVE THEM FROM THE WALLS!

THE PALACE _CAN_ BE HELD!

WE WILL CALL UP OUR SUPPORTERS FROM THE CITY!

BUT **THEN** WHAT?

THE KING IS SO **ILL**.

AND IF HE DIES, IT IS THE PRINCE'S RIGHTFUL PLACE...

HE WILL HAVE US **FLAYED**!

THERE IS NO ROOM FOR THAT SORT OF THINKING, THOMPSON!

NO, NO, CAPTAIN, I DON'T MEAN _THAT_.

I WILL CERTAINLY DIE BEFORE **KANGAR** RULES MY HAND!

BUT WHAT ARE WE TO DO? —IT SEEMS SUCH A HOPELESS BATTLE...

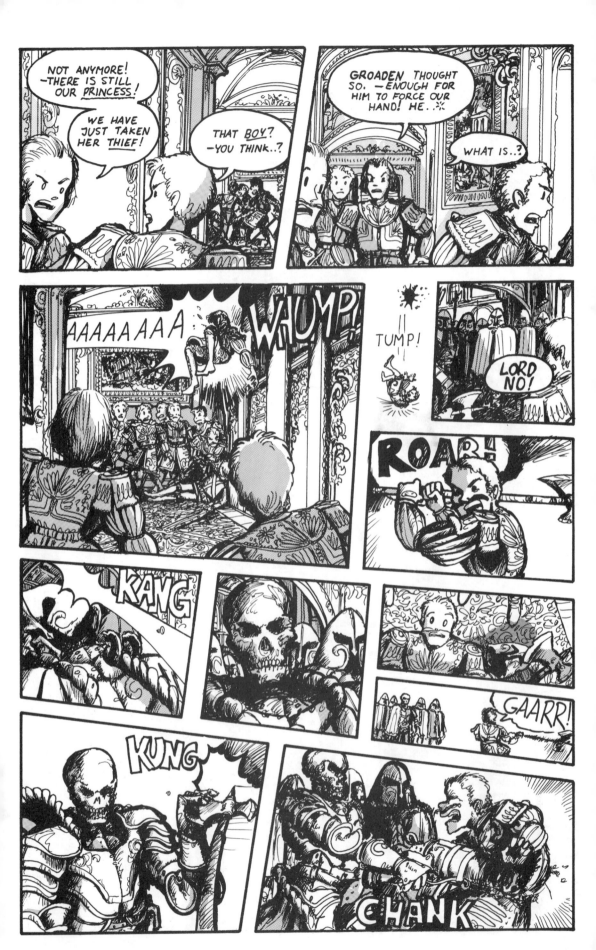

NO..!

THE PRINCE HAS FOUND SOME WAY TO BRING HIS ENSORCELLED IRON INTO THE PALACE!

BUT HOW?! THE PALACE HAS ALWAYS BEEN ABLE TO RESIST..!

THIS IS DARK THIS IS DARK!

PULL BACK MEN!

DO NOT ENGAGE!!

TO THE KING!

FALL BACK TO HIS MAJESTY'S SUITE! WE MUST TAKE THE KING FROM THE PALACE!

WE MUST ESCAPE!

CAPTAIN

THE IRON GUARD HAVE COME! —ON THE SOUTH AND WEST TOWER WALKS!

—THEY ARE IN THE PALACE!

BILLARN AND JACOB HAVE BEEN KILLED!

DAMN! THEY ARE ON US! —WE HAVE BEEN BARRICADED!

FALL BACK!

RETREAT! RETREAT!

RETREAT!

Not long...

Not long...

Rubel...

Chapter 2

WHATCHA DOING?

ONE THOUSAND YEARS AGO IN A SMALL BOROUG CALLED MILLBROOK...

DIGGING.

CAN I HELP?

YOU'LL GET YOUR DRESS DIRTY.

BUT I'M NOT WEARING A DRESS.

I HAVE TROUSERS ON TODAY.

YOUR MOM LETS YOU WEAR TROUSERS?

SHE DOES SOMETIMES.

WELL, OKAY THEN. YOU CAN DIG FOR A WHILE IF YOU WANT.

I'M TIRED ANYWAY.

GOODEY!

WHAT ARE WE DIGGING FOR?

TREASURE.

WOW! TREASURE? REALLY?

YUP! IT'S GOING TO BE RIGHT DOWN IN THAT HOLE.

IN OUR YARD?

ARE YOU SURE?

WHY WOULD ANYBODY BURY TREASURE IN OUR YARD?

'CAUSE IT'S A GREAT HIDING PLACE...

WHO'D THINK TO LOOK HERE?

YEAH, I SUPPOSE SO...

I GUESS...

HOW DO WE KNOW WHICH ONE OF THESE IS THE CURSED ONE?

WE DON'T! —WE'LL BURY THEM ALL!

DON'T THOSE BELONG TO LADY LOCUMIRE?

NOT ANYMORE!! SHOVEL AWAY!

CHAN K

WE'LL SEND A TREASURE MAP TO THE KING, AND HE'LL SEND HIS KNIGHTS TO DIG IT UP AND TAKE IT AWAY TO HIS TREASURE VAULTS WHERE IT CAN'T DO ANY HARM!

TANGLE WITH QUINTON ZEMPFESTER, WILL SHE?! HA!

I'LL SICK CROWN TREASURE LAW ON HER!

I'D JUST LIKE TO SEE HER TRY TO BREAK INTO THE KING'S OWN VAULTS!

OOHHH. I'LL BE GLAD WHEN THIS IS ALL OVER!

I DO SO HATE ALL THIS PROTECTING THE LAND FROM EVIL BUSINESS!

IT WAS MUCH SIMPLER BEFORE YOU CAME TO STAY, WHEN WE JUST LET THINGS BE!

YOU'RE JUST LUCKY I SHOWED UP WHEN I DID!

IGNORANCE MAY BE BLISS, BUT IT CAN ALSO GET YOU KILLED!

I KNOW, BUT SO CAN WITCHES.

YOU KNOW, I ALWAYS SORT OF WONDERED, BUT I NEVER KNEW FOR SURE...

IS LADY LOCUMIRE REALLY A WITCH?

YEAH. SHE HAS SECRET PASSAGES AND EVERYTHING!

SHE DOES? WOW. CAN I GO WITH YOU NEXT TIME?

NEXT TIME?? WHAT DO YOU MEAN NEXT TIME? THERE IS NO NEXT TIME!

QUINTON?!

HMM... HEATH MAY BE RIGHT.

EVEN AS WE SPEAK, THE EVIL LOCUMIRE IS LIKELY PLOTTING HER REVENGE!

WE NEED ALL THE TRUSTWORTHY HANDS WE CAN GET IN OUR NEVER-ENDING BATTLE AGAINST EVIL.

I MOVE WE GRANT HEATH FULL RECOGNITION AND MEMBERSHIP INTO THE SECRET SOCIETY OF MONSTER SLAYERS.

NEVERENDING?! YOU NEVER SAID IT WAS GOING TO BE NEVER-ENDING!

HOLD ON! YOU GUYS HAVE A SECRET SOCIETY, AND YOU NEVER TOLD ME!?

IT WAS A SECRET.

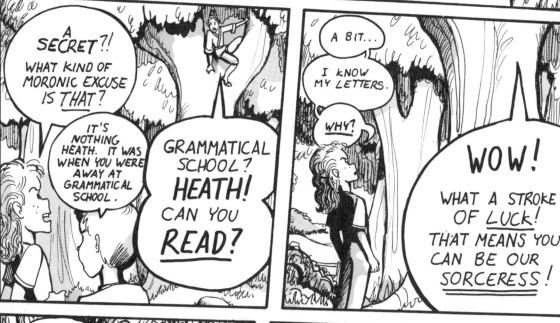

A SECRET?! WHAT KIND OF MORONIC EXCUSE IS THAT?

IT'S NOTHING HEATH. IT WAS WHEN YOU WERE AWAY AT GRAMMATICAL SCHOOL.

GRAMMATICAL SCHOOL? HEATH! CAN YOU READ?

A BIT... I KNOW MY LETTERS.

WHY?

WOW! WHAT A STROKE OF LUCK! THAT MEANS YOU CAN BE OUR SORCERESS!

I'VE BEEN LOOKING FOR A NEW APPRENTICE! -FINNLY HAS A STOUT AND NOBLE HEART, BUT HE LACKS THE NECESSARY APTITUDE FOR THE MYSTIC ARTS.

HUMPH! THANK GOODNESS! -I HOPE THAT MEANS NO MORE DRAGON HUNTS!

NO OFFENCE, BUT I NEVER LIKED ANY OF THIS 'APPRENTICE' STUFF.

AS FAR AS I'M CONCERNED, YOU CAN KEEP YOUR MAGIC!

YOU MEAN I CAN LEARN MAGIC? REAL MAGIC?

SURE, IF YOU'RE INTERESTED.

BOY! AM I EVER!

ALL IN FAVOR OF AMENDING THE SECRET CHARTER TO ACCEPT HEATH INTO OUR NOBLE FOLD, SAY 'I'.

'I'.

'I'.

NOW HOLD ON A MOMENT!

I'M NOT AGREEING TO ANYTHING THAT WOULD PUT MISS HEATH INTO DANGER!

IT'S BAD ENOUGH THAT YOU HAVE ME AND DAVIN RUNNING ABOUT AFTER ALL THESE FRIGHTFUL EVILS. —AND WITHOUT ANY PROPER TRAINING I MIGHT ADD..!

BUT I'D NEVER BE ABLE TO FACE MYSELF IF WE HAD TO GO TELL MRS. JAY THAT HEATH WAS EATEN BY A DRAGON!

YOU GUYS HAVE FOUGHT DRAGONS?!

NO WE HAVEN'T.

IT TURNED OUT JUST TO BE MR. MOLTON. —THEY CAUGHT HIM IN A TREE!

THE BAILIFF HAD TO COME AND CUT HIM DOWN!

AND HE MADE QUINTON AND FINNLY PULL ALL THE WEEDS OUT FROM IN FRONT OF THE TOWN HALL.

THE BAILIFF?! YOU GOT ARRESTED?

IT WAS THE MOST EMBARRASSING EXPERIENCE OF MY WHOLE LIFE!

YEAH, WELL THEY NEVER PROVED HE WASN'T A SHAPE CHANGING DRAGON!

AND IF YOU ASK ME, THAT OLD BLOWHARD, MOLTON, COULD HAVE USED A BIT OF HANGING IN A NET ANYWAY!

EITHER WAY, I DON'T MIND PULLING WEEDS FOR A DAY IF IT MEANS THE VILLAGE CAN SLEEP SAFELY AT NIGHT!

IT'S THE PRICE YOU MUST SOMETIMES BE PREPARED TO PAY FOR FACING THE FORCES OF DARKNESS!

WOW. I HAVE GOT TO JOIN THIS CLUB.

BUT MISS HEATH, THINK OF YOUR AUNT AND HOW SHE'LL WORRY!

BUT IT'S A SECRET SOCIETY. HOW WILL SHE EVEN KNOW?

GASP!

OH MY LORD! WHAT HAVE YOU DONE TO THE YARD?!

AH! MRS. JAY! —HAVE YOU COME WITH THAT EXTRA SHOVEL I REQUESTED?

Chapter 3

Upon the wall there was a picture.

In the picture, there was a shadow.

It watched from within and Rubel, unable to do anything else, watched it back. It moved and watched and moved again, doing so with the same silky, heavy motion common in the sort of cats that live in jungles.

The name of this beast was Jurid, but Rubel did not know that. He knew only to watch it and rock gently on his heels while the world grew fuzzy in his vision and the blood clotted around the stub of metal in his side.

Through the haze of his perception, he could hear the majesty guard outside the door barking to one another in tight voices; men of acute patriotic devotion and ability who, as the enemy pressed them, quickly lost the roguish attitude they had born when their strength and casual efficiency had easily outmatched that of prince Kangar's blue backs.

Before such juggernaut force as the iron clad giants, the men under lieutenant captain Earl Muroe's command fell back. They fell back until, for some reason not altogether clear to Rubel but which seemed of the utmost importance to the soldiers, the retreat was called to a halt. With a tense command, Muroe's men raced off and produced heavy swords and war axes and iron shafted spears from hidden caches, (all weapons made for two hands).

Three very large and very old bolt lock cannons were brought out from dusty window closets; guns which had been designed at one time to be used against such things as dragons and other airborne targets, (the likes of which nobody had seen for many countless ages, and which explained the great degree to which the canons had been allowed to decay). —Only one of them was serviceable at all, while the other two seized hopelessly, rusted at every moving part.

This single cannon was dragged with hasty effort into position at the head of a stairwell, leaving long and ugly scrapes upon the polished wooden floor. Armed with one of the antique iron missile shafts also rescued from the dust, the cannon was brought into action. Its mere presence had a powerful bolstering effect upon the king's soldiers. Their hearts all sprang as one, each man made giddy by both a racing heart and the sudden possibility that the battle might be turning in their favor.

According to old wisdom passed down and held in the stores of knowledge kept by such groups as the majesty guard, the enchanted iron warriors could, in theory, be destroyed. It required that the great helm of an undead soldier be smashed or wrenched away and that the skeleton head once exposed be severed at the neck with an aptly swung blade.

Of course, this could only be achieved at great personal risk to the attacking party, but the majesty guard existed for precisely such purposes, and they set themselves upon the task with a murderous energy.

Two iron guards were successfully annihilated in this manner, (one of which had already lost its helmet), and a third was toppled in a thunderous crash as the bolt lock cannon hurled its missile, smashing it through the breast plate of the giant. The king's men let out a grand hurrah as each behemoth fell, and for several breathless moments it seemed to all that the battle might indeed be won.

But this was not to be.

The cannon, in discharging, had damaged itself beyond further use, and the warrior it had struck did not stay down. Though with a shattered cavity in its chest, the iron beast brought itself back up again. Glaring in cold fury upon the king's men, the behemoth resumed its advance, crushing a wounded man to death with one terrible tromp of its mighty foot. Another raised its own great weapon and loosed all six chambers into a knot of soldiers still struggling with the broken canon.

And so it went, the loss of life escalating at such an alarming rate that the majesty guard would certainly have been exterminated had not Muroe raised his voice. He had been watching the killing with a terrible anxiety. —The sort you feel when horrible things are happening, but which you cannot stop until a foolish, and incidental task is completed. (In this case, it was the rescuing of some documents and the destruction of some others; papers and maps which had almost been forgotten in the fray, and which could under no circumstances be left to the enemy). And so, with this foolish task secured, he gave at last the command to resume their retreat and abandon the palace. —A move he knew which carried with it vast ramifications.

f least importance, the decision meant giving up their foothold within the castle. —Even though such a position would prove extremely difficult to regain once lost, the palace could never be entirely closed off to the majesty guard. If they felt like fighting hard enough then, even with the drawbridge up and all the windows shuttered tight, the palace could still be taken back. It was possible because of hidden passage ways and secret doors.

Within the castle architecture there existed such secret and mystical elements as were known to only a very few. Of course, owing to both the enormous age of the palace and to the genius with which it had been constructed, a great many of those secrets had been forgotten long, long ago. The majesty guard was, however, a brotherhood spanning nearly three centuries. —And while three hundred years might not seem like much when measured against the age of the palace, (which was very much older, indeed), it was certainly long enough for a company of clever men to acquire at least a few secrets. And it was one of those very secrets through which Muroe intended to evacuate both the king and his men.

So the real significance, Muroe knew, did not lie in actually leaving the palace to the enemy. It did not lie in the strategic placement of troops or guns. The real significance was of a less tangible variety, though one which struck a deep chord in his heart.

There is a type of special person who, while their gift may seem at first to be of wonderful advantage, actually finds it more difficult to excel in positions of high responsibility than another person might. Muroe was one of these.

Muroe had exceptional 'sight'. Subtle or gross, he was able to see quite clearly the currents and moods of a society acting upon its people. Currents and moods which were often virtually invisible to others. And it caused him to worry. Out of natural habit, he always tried to sort out how best to position himself in the unceasing flow of time and events so that he might help things work out in ways that were right and good.

He was always so *serious,* people would accuse. And he had become even more so of late. Despite his best efforts, events were right then barreling down a route he had long ago foreseen. In Muroe's eyes, quitting the palace was final proof of more than just a battle gone sour.

our years ago when prince Kangar was just 13 years old, the boy asked his father if he might be granted a division of soldiers for his very own. —A group of soldiers who would be like his father's majesty guard, except that Kangar would call them the 'prince guard' and they would only be for him. The king was not happy about this idea at all.

The king had grown of late to find the job of being a father an increasingly difficult one. True, it had never been easy for him to love and trust his young son, but in recent years things had gotten worse.

Small children have many ways to show when they are angry, but usually a fit of rage is quickly over and then easily put aside, both by the child and parent alike. The times, however, were coming to an end when the king's children could only run and deal with their anger in the small ways allowed to children. Kangar was on the verge of turning into a young man with all the powers young men have, and as this time approached, things became decidedly strained between father and son.

On occasion, the king would attempt to prove to his son, (as well as to himself), that he really did trust and love the boy, just as much as he perceived good fathers ought. So he granted Kangar his wish and gave him some soldiers, quietly hoping that doing so would provide Kangar with a place into which all those unhappy energies with which the boy was so filled might be channeled and transformed into something healthy and good. The king had no extraordinary wisdom, but he did know that sometimes happiness and contentment could be found when a person toils upon something loved.

And so, dressed in finely cut uniforms of brand new design and rich blue material, sixty men were selected and granted titles and stations in their own small division, and they were given over to the prince to be commanded as the boy saw fit. Kangar was delighted. He paraded his beaming new soldiers up and down the streets of the city, much to the satisfaction of the people, who loved him. And though the king felt ill at ease, the man smiled and waved to his son.

It was during this uneasy time that a great blow was dealt to the king for which he was entirely unprepared. His daughter, princess Katara, ran away into the Sleeping Wood where no one and no effort could find her.

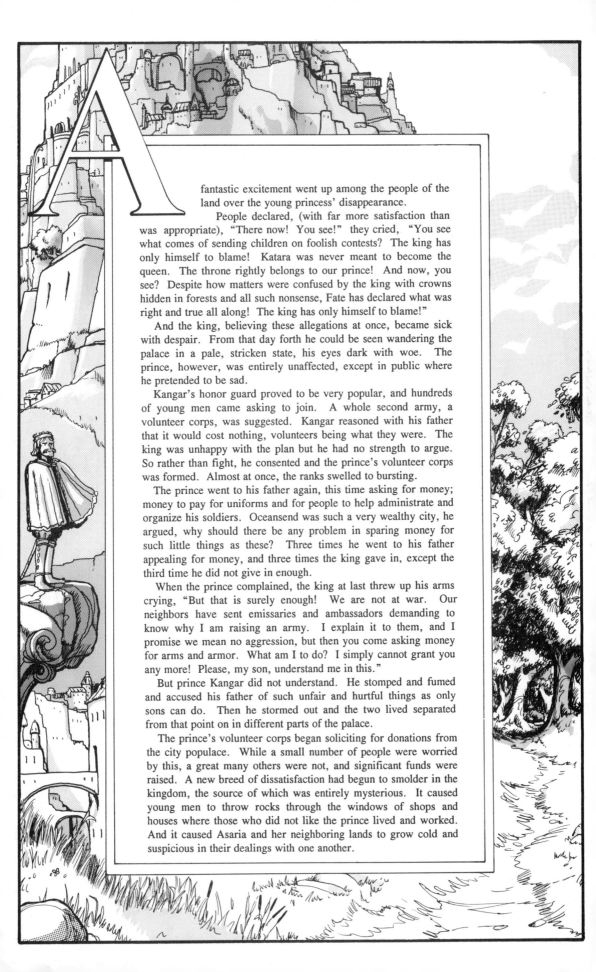

A fantastic excitement went up among the people of the land over the young princess' disappearance.

People declared, (with far more satisfaction than was appropriate), "There now! You see!" they cried, "You see what comes of sending children on foolish contests? The king has only himself to blame! Katara was never meant to become the queen. The throne rightly belongs to our prince! And now, you see? Despite how matters were confused by the king with crowns hidden in forests and all such nonsense, Fate has declared what was right and true all along! The king has only himself to blame!"

And the king, believing these allegations at once, became sick with despair. From that day forth he could be seen wandering the palace in a pale, stricken state, his eyes dark with woe. The prince, however, was entirely unaffected, except in public where he pretended to be sad.

Kangar's honor guard proved to be very popular, and hundreds of young men came asking to join. A whole second army, a volunteer corps, was suggested. Kangar reasoned with his father that it would cost nothing, volunteers being what they were. The king was unhappy with the plan but he had no strength to argue. So rather than fight, he consented and the prince's volunteer corps was formed. Almost at once, the ranks swelled to bursting.

The prince went to his father again, this time asking for money; money to pay for uniforms and for people to help administrate and organize his soldiers. Oceansend was such a very wealthy city, he argued, why should there be any problem in sparing money for such little things as these? Three times he went to his father appealing for money, and three times the king gave in, except the third time he did not give in enough.

When the prince complained, the king at last threw up his arms crying, "But that is surely enough! We are not at war. Our neighbors have sent emissaries and ambassadors demanding to know why I am raising an army. I explain it to them, and I promise we mean no aggression, but then you come asking money for arms and armor. What am I to do? I simply cannot grant you any more! Please, my son, understand me in this."

But prince Kangar did not understand. He stomped and fumed and accused his father of such unfair and hurtful things as only sons can do. Then he stormed out and the two lived separated from that point on in different parts of the palace.

The prince's volunteer corps began soliciting for donations from the city populace. While a small number of people were worried by this, a great many others were not, and significant funds were raised. A new breed of dissatisfaction had begun to smolder in the kingdom, the source of which was entirely mysterious. It caused young men to throw rocks through the windows of shops and houses where those who did not like the prince lived and worked. And it caused Asaria and her neighboring lands to grow cold and suspicious in their dealings with one another.

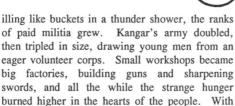

Filling like buckets in a thunder shower, the ranks of paid militia grew. Kangar's army doubled, then tripled in size, drawing young men from an eager volunteer corps. Small workshops became big factories, building guns and sharpening swords, and all the while the strange hunger burned higher in the hearts of the people. With very little effort the prince had in but three and a half years, come to occupy a position of high authority and rapidly increasing power.

The king woke up each morning with more and more worries, and a paler and paler face until, on the very same morning of the prince's 17th birthday, the king did not wake up at all. Laboring beneath the pall of his strange illness, the simple man with his simple heart lay in a tortured, murmuring state, doomed to waste away while doctors administered liquids directly into his body through a set of ugly metal tubes. That same day, the iron guard, donned in brilliant red capes, made their first appearance, marching in the prince's birthday parade.

The mysterious armored giants were admired and feared by all for their strength and silent devotion to the rising prince, who would surely soon be king. The people cheered and prince Kangar shone before them in military dress, young and handsome with his sword and breast plate flashing in the sun.

And so, in flanks which held the tops of stairwells and hallways leading to the king's suite, the majesty guard fell back. Each flank doing its best to protect the one before it.

While the official documents and ceremonies were perhaps weeks or even many months away from being signed and performed, Muroe knew that this morning marked the true end of his master's rein. The man he was sworn to protect had been brought to the very brink of death, and Muroe had been unable to stop it.

But there were *other* forces at work. Forces which ran deeper than did the knowledge of the majesty guard. There were *thieves*. Thieves of an old cast and mind. And if the most secret whispers were true, then the princess herself had such a thief beneath her rule; there was the strange boy, of whom Muroe knew precious little, and until that morning had even doubted the existence of, (and if the truth were known, doubted even now). But whatever the case, the prince was frightened of that boy. And that was something in a day when the prince feared neither his father nor the might of other nations.

Indeed, there was still the princess.

GET UP. WE MUST LEAVE AT ONCE!

YOU WILL BE KILLED IF YOU STAY HERE! CAN YOU WALK?

QUICKLY!

THERE ISN'T ANY TIME!

GO! GO RUBEL! THIS IS SERIOUS!

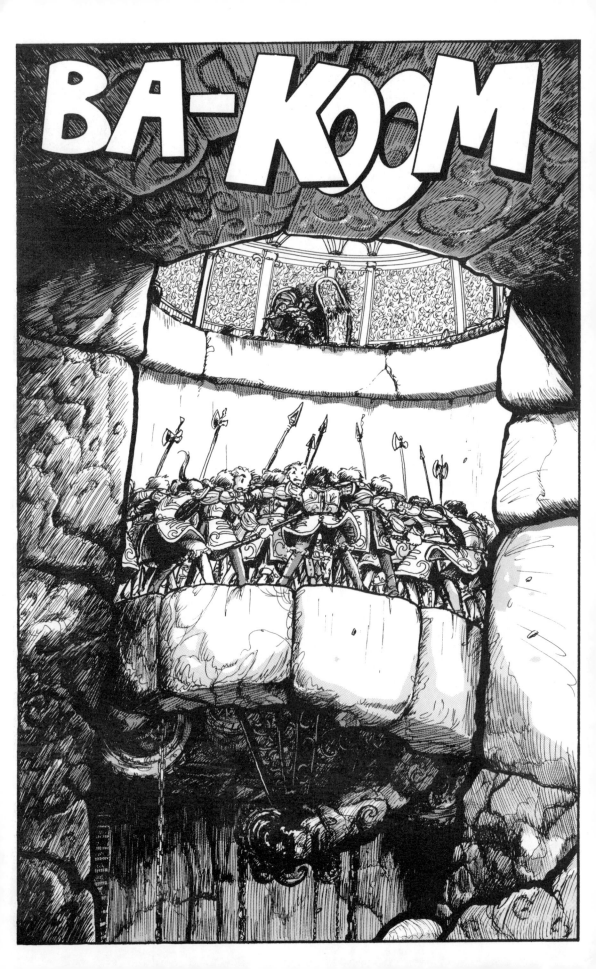

IT ISN'T HURTING SO BAD ANYMORE, BUT IT'S STILL POKING OUT OF ME.

POKING..?

LORD! AND HE'S STILL *STANDING*!

WE'LL HAVE TO REMOVE THAT ONCE WE'VE REACHED SAFETY.

—WE ARE THE KING'S HONOR GUARD.

YOU CAN THROW YOUR TRUST IN WITH US, SO LONG AS YOU ARE TRUE TO THE KING.

YOU *ARE* PRINCESS KATARA'S CHOSEN SERVANT?

SERVANT?

MY NAME IS RUBEL, AND I AM HER *THIEF*, AND I AM TRUE TO *HER*, *NOT* THE KING.

I WILL ONLY TRUST IN YOU SO LONG AS YOU MEAN *HER* NO HARM.

I TOOK A SOLDIER'S *LIFE* TODAY BECAUSE HE SAID HOW MUCH HE WANTED TO *KILL* THE PRINCESS.

I AM AT WAR WITH *ANY* SOLDIER WHO WOULD BEAR ARMS AGAINST KATARA!

—SO! IS *THAT* HOW YOU GOT SHOT?

HUM! I'LL WARN YOU, —I DON'T SUFFER FOOLS PATIENTLY!

FOOLS? WHAT ARE YOU TALKING ABOUT?

WHAT? —YOU THINK I SHOULDN'T FIGHT A GUY IF HE WANTS TO KILL KATARA?

WHAT IF SOME GUY TOLD YOU HE WANTED TO KILL THE *KING*? —RIGHT TO YOUR FACE?

—AND IF HE WAS SAYING OTHER BAD STUFF AS WELL?

THEN I'D HAVE CHALLENGED HIS WORD! THAT'S FOR CERTAIN! —PERHAPS I'D EVEN *ARREST* HIM. BUT I'D NOT STRIKE A MAN *DEAD*!

NOT JUST FOR *WORDS*!

YOU DON'T *KILL* A MAN FOR CALLING NAMES!

IT WASN'T JUST NAMES! —HE HAD HIS **SWORD** DRAWN AGAINST ME!

AND I ONLY KILLED _HIM_. —I COULD'VE FOUGHT ALL THE OTHERS TOO, BUT I DIDN'T!

ANYWAY, THAT'S NOT EVEN HOW I GOT SHOT!

YOU DON'T KNOW ANYTHING.

FAIR ENOUGH. —I SUPPOSE WE ARE **ALL** AT WAR NOW...

HAVE WE ALL COME THROUGH?

THEN TRIP THE VAULT STONES!

WE WILL SEAL THIS PASSAGE BEHIND US!

CLUNK

GRNNNN

BOOM

LET'S GET MOVING THEN

WE'VE A LONG WAY TO GO BEFORE WE CAN REST. THE PALACE ISN'T SAFE ANYMORE.

NOT EVEN HERE.

COME ON.

Chapter 4

ONE THOUSAND YEARS AGO IN A SMALL BOROUGH CALLED MILLBROOK...

YOU STUPID LITTLE TWERP! THAT'S NOT TRUE!

IT IS TOO!

IT IS NOT!

YEAH? WELL MY DAD SAYS IT IS!

YEAH? WELL MAYBE YOUR DAD'S AN IDIOT!

HEY, QUINTON! THIS STUPID KID SAYS YOU KILLED SOME GUY.

HE'S LYING, RIGHT?

WHAT?!

STROVEN THE DEPRAVED?! IT CAN'T BE!!

STROVEN THE DEPRAVED?

I DENY EVERYTHING!

I WAS FRAMED!

IT WENT OFF IN MY HAND!

I PLEAD INSANITY!

WHAT?! -HAVE HIS HENCHMEN COME FOR ME?

HE STILL HAS HENCHMEN?

MY DAD SAYS THAT YOU KILLED A MAILMAN.

YOU HAVE TO SWEAR

DO YOU?

I SWEAR.

GOOD.

NOW, IF YOU'LL EXCUSE ME, I WAS ON MY WAY TO GO FISHING.

—FISHING IS A GOOD WAY TO CLEAR THE MIND. —IT'LL HELP ME PLAN WHAT TO DO ABOUT LOCUMIRE.

SHE'S STILL GOT TOO MUCH POWER, AND I HAVE TO FIGURE SOME WAY TO SORT HER OUT.

WOW. I SHOULD COME TOO THEN, SINCE I'M YOUR APPRENTICE SORCERESS.

YEAH, THAT'S A GOOD IDEA.

CAN I COME TOO?

NO! YOU'RE NOT PART OF THE GROUP!

'FRAID SHE'S RIGHT. —BUT YOU CAN COME AND DIG WORMS IF YOU LIKE.

OKAY!

BUT QUINTON! HE SHOULDN'T HEAR! —HE MIGHT TELL!

I WOULDN'T TELL!

WHY WOULD HE TELL? —HE SWORE ALREADY.

YEAH! I SWORE ALREADY!

BUT QUINTON!

HE'S JUST A STUPID KID! —HE'LL FORGET AND TELL SOMEBODY! YOU COULD GET IN TROUBLE!

WHAT IF LOCUMIRE FINDS OUT?!

I WON'T TELL LOCUMIRE! I WOULDN'T FORGET!

WHERE DID I PUT THAT FISHING ROD..?

WHAT'S YOUR NAME, KID?

TIMMY

HEATH! TIMMY!

GO GET SOME FISHING POLES AND MEET ME AT THE POND!

SIGH...

HEY THERE. WHERE'S THAT KID?

I DUNNO. HE TOOK OFF.

WHAT'S THE MATTER HEATH?

YOU BEEN FIGHTING?

THAT STUPID KID SAID HE WAS GOING TO TELL ON YOU.

AW, LITTLE KIDS ARE LIKE THAT SOMETIMES.

DON'T WORRY ABOUT IT.

HE'S TOO SMALL TO CAUSE MUCH TROUBLE.

BUT I SAID HE WOULDN'T KEEP IT A SECRET!

WE SHOULDN'T HAVE TOLD HIM!

WELL, YOU NEVER KNOW.

SOMETIMES PEOPLE CAN SURPRISE YOU, BUT YOU HAVE TO GIVE THEM THE CHANCE FIRST.

YOU FIND OUT PRETTY FAST HOW MUCH YOU CAN DEPEND ON SOMEONE.

MMM...

YOU CAN DEPEND ON *ME* PRETTY FAR, THOUGH, RIGHT?

OH, *DEFINITELY.*

YOU AND DAVIN AND FINNLY ARE MY BEST FRIENDS IN THIS WHOLE PLACE!

AND YOU'RE A *SORCERESS,* SO THERE'S DEPENDABILITY RIGHT THERE.

YEAH...

EXCEPT...

YOU HAVEN'T TAUGHT ME ANY MAGIC YET.

YEAH, I GUESS IT'S ABOUT TIME.

WE'LL START TOMORROW.

BUT HEATH... I THINK TODAY WE SHOULD JUST *FISH.*

OKAY?

YEAH.

OKAY.

Chapter 5

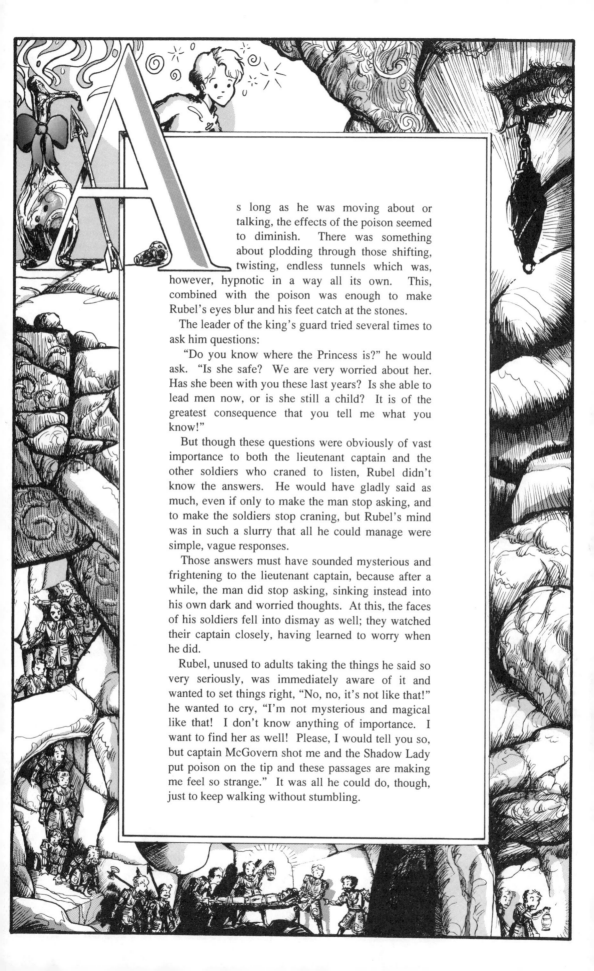

As long as he was moving about or talking, the effects of the poison seemed to diminish. There was something about plodding through those shifting, twisting, endless tunnels which was, however, hypnotic in a way all its own. This, combined with the poison was enough to make Rubel's eyes blur and his feet catch at the stones.

The leader of the king's guard tried several times to ask him questions:

"Do you know where the Princess is?" he would ask. "Is she safe? We are very worried about her. Has she been with you these last years? Is she able to lead men now, or is she still a child? It is of the greatest consequence that you tell me what you know!"

But though these questions were obviously of vast importance to both the lieutenant captain and the other soldiers who craned to listen, Rubel didn't know the answers. He would have gladly said as much, even if only to make the man stop asking, and to make the soldiers stop craning, but Rubel's mind was in such a slurry that all he could manage were simple, vague responses.

Those answers must have sounded mysterious and frightening to the lieutenant captain, because after a while, the man did stop asking, sinking instead into his own dark and worried thoughts. At this, the faces of his soldiers fell into dismay as well; they watched their captain closely, having learned to worry when he did.

Rubel, unused to adults taking the things he said so very seriously, was immediately aware of it and wanted to set things right, "No, no, it's not like that!" he wanted to cry, "I'm not mysterious and magical like that! I don't know anything of importance. I want to find her as well! Please, I would tell you so, but captain McGovern shot me and the Shadow Lady put poison on the tip and these passages are making me feel so strange." It was all he could do, though, just to keep walking without stumbling.

Every shadow cast by all the many lanterns flickered and danced over the stones, drawing Rubel further away from reality and deeper into his mesmerized state. He began to smell fresh things in the air; flowers and grass, and there seemed to be warmth where there should not have been, all deep within the mountain.

Every now and then the passage would open from beneath the stone, out into the blinding daylight and crisp air so that the lanterns flickered like pale ghost flames and the soldiers squinted and blinked over the city sprawled below. These brief bursts of light and fresh air revived Rubel somewhat, but each time, his head soon flowed back into the dark, warm swirls of the poison.

PSST!

?

PSST! THIEF!

YOU MUST COME AWAY!

WE MUST SPEAK!

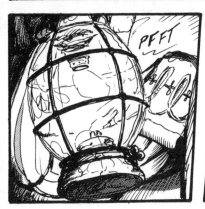

PFFT

HEY!

?!?

WHAT'S THIS?

WHAT'S WRONG?!

CAPTAIN..?

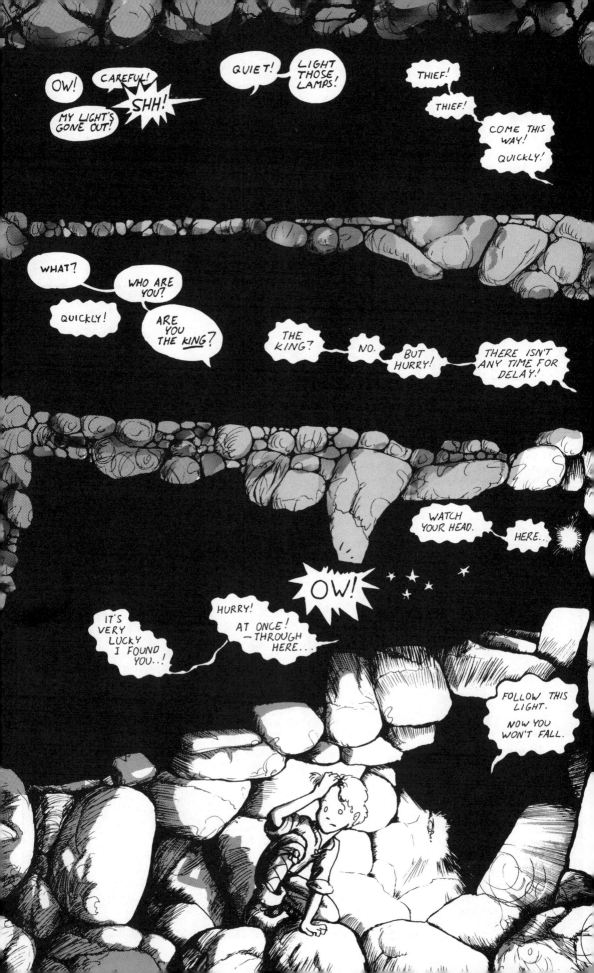

HEH, HEH.

THOUGHT YOU WERE PRETTY **SMART**, DIDN'T YOU?

THIEVES ALWAYS DO.

BUT WHAT CAN *YOU* DO?

YOU'RE ALL ALONE IN THE DARK WITHOUT...

HEY, WHAT ARE YOU..?

NO

NO!

STOP!

YOU CAN'T **DO** THAT!

NO FAIR!

OW!

GIVE IT BACK!

HA! I **THOUGHT** SO!

YOU'RE A CAVE-TROLL!

YEAH, **SO**?

THAT DOESN'T MEAN YOU CAN JUST GO AROUND STEALING EVERYBODY'S LAMP!

THIS LAMP ISN'T EVEN **YOURS**!

YOU'RE THE ONE WHO **STOLE** IT!

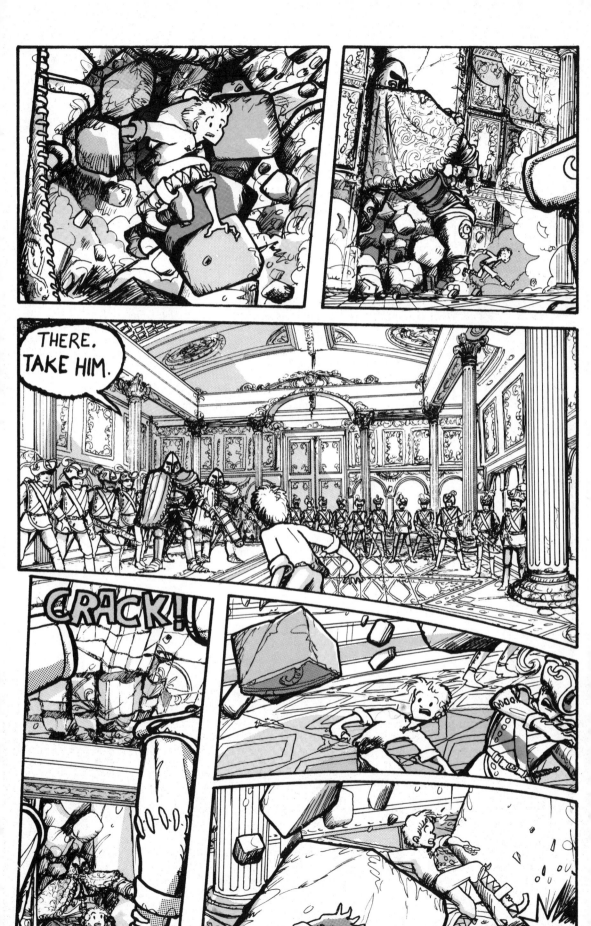

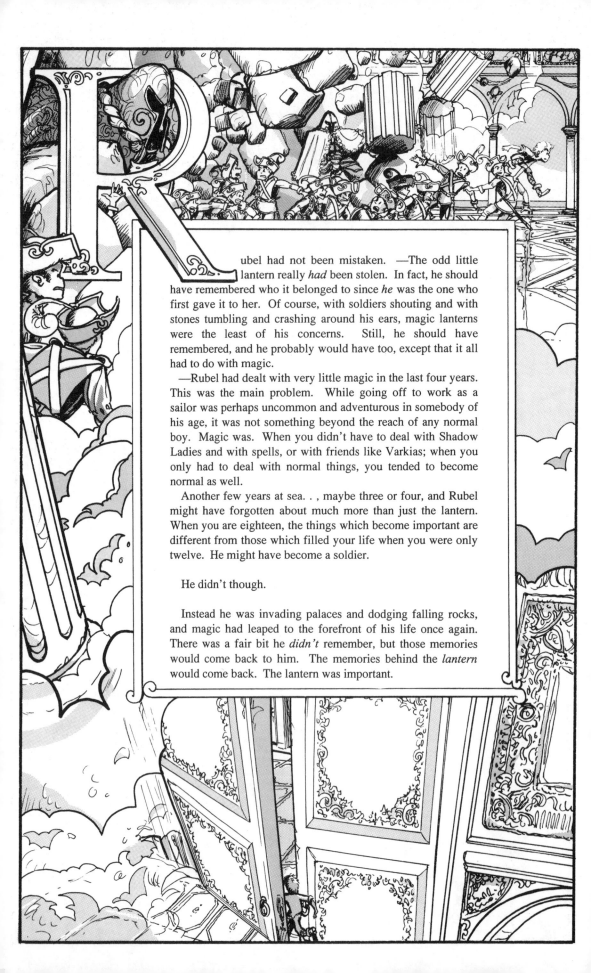

ubel had not been mistaken. —The odd little
lantern really *had* been stolen. In fact, he should
have remembered who it belonged to since *he* was the one who
first gave it to her. Of course, with soldiers shouting and with
stones tumbling and crashing around his ears, magic lanterns
were the least of his concerns. Still, he should have
remembered, and he probably would have too, except that it all
had to do with magic.

—Rubel had dealt with very little magic in the last four years.
This was the main problem. While going off to work as a
sailor was perhaps uncommon and adventurous in somebody of
his age, it was not something beyond the reach of any normal
boy. Magic was. When you didn't have to deal with Shadow
Ladies and with spells, or with friends like Varkias; when you
only had to deal with normal things, you tended to become
normal as well.

Another few years at sea. . , maybe three or four, and Rubel
might have forgotten about much more than just the lantern.
When you are eighteen, the things which become important are
different from those which filled your life when you were only
twelve. He might have become a soldier.

He didn't though.

Instead he was invading palaces and dodging falling rocks,
and magic had leaped to the forefront of his life once again.
There was a fair bit he *didn't* remember, but those memories
would come back to him. The memories behind the *lantern*
would come back. The lantern was important.

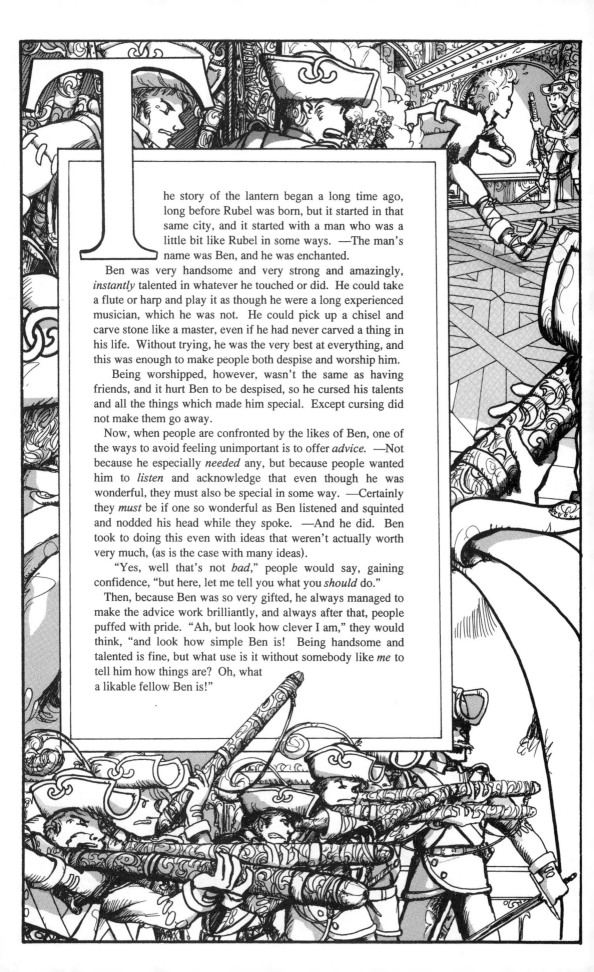

he story of the lantern began a long time ago, long before Rubel was born, but it started in that same city, and it started with a man who was a little bit like Rubel in some ways. —The man's name was Ben, and he was enchanted.

Ben was very handsome and very strong and amazingly, *instantly* talented in whatever he touched or did. He could take a flute or harp and play it as though he were a long experienced musician, which he was not. He could pick up a chisel and carve stone like a master, even if he had never carved a thing in his life. Without trying, he was the very best at everything, and this was enough to make people both despise and worship him.

Being worshipped, however, wasn't the same as having friends, and it hurt Ben to be despised, so he cursed his talents and all the things which made him special. Except cursing did not make them go away.

Now, when people are confronted by the likes of Ben, one of the ways to avoid feeling unimportant is to offer *advice.* —Not because he especially *needed* any, but because people wanted him to *listen* and acknowledge that even though he was wonderful, they must also be special in some way. —Certainly they *must* be if one so wonderful as Ben listened and squinted and nodded his head while they spoke. —And he did. Ben took to doing this even with ideas that weren't actually worth very much, (as is the case with many ideas).

"Yes, well that's not *bad*," people would say, gaining confidence, "but here, let me tell you what you *should* do."

Then, because Ben was so very gifted, he always managed to make the advice work brilliantly, and always after that, people puffed with pride. "Ah, but look how clever I am," they would think, "and look how simple Ben is! Being handsome and talented is fine, but what use is it without somebody like *me* to tell him how things are? Oh, what a likable fellow Ben is!"

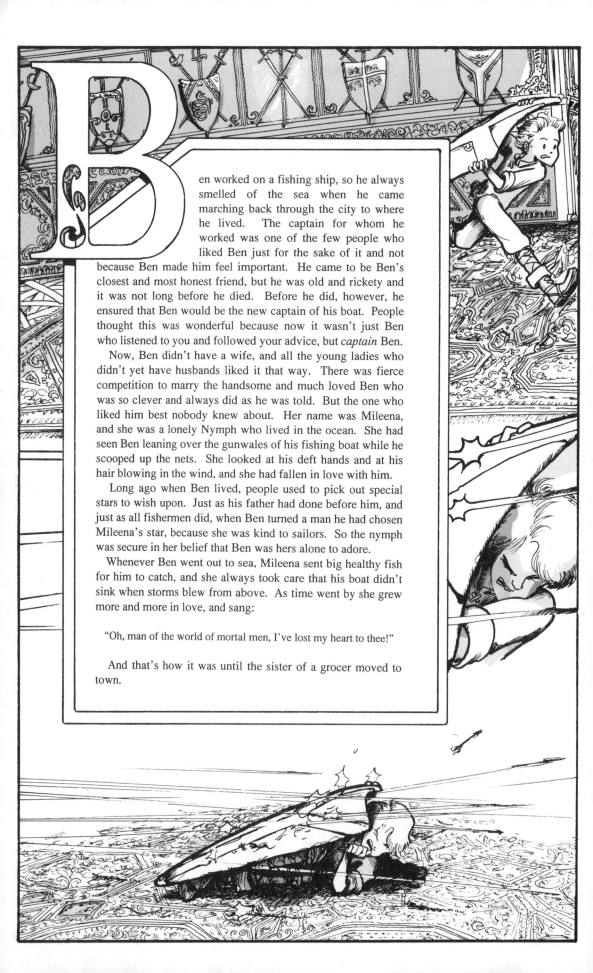

Ben worked on a fishing ship, so he always smelled of the sea when he came marching back through the city to where he lived. The captain for whom he worked was one of the few people who liked Ben just for the sake of it and not because Ben made him feel important. He came to be Ben's closest and most honest friend, but he was old and rickety and it was not long before he died. Before he did, however, he ensured that Ben would be the new captain of his boat. People thought this was wonderful because now it wasn't just Ben who listened to you and followed your advice, but *captain* Ben.

Now, Ben didn't have a wife, and all the young ladies who didn't yet have husbands liked it that way. There was fierce competition to marry the handsome and much loved Ben who was so clever and always did as he was told. But the one who liked him best nobody knew about. Her name was Mileena, and she was a lonely Nymph who lived in the ocean. She had seen Ben leaning over the gunwales of his fishing boat while he scooped up the nets. She looked at his deft hands and at his hair blowing in the wind, and she had fallen in love with him.

Long ago when Ben lived, people used to pick out special stars to wish upon. Just as his father had done before him, and just as all fishermen did, when Ben turned a man he had chosen Mileena's star, because she was kind to sailors. So the nymph was secure in her belief that Ben was hers alone to adore.

Whenever Ben went out to sea, Mileena sent big healthy fish for him to catch, and she always took care that his boat didn't sink when storms blew from above. As time went by she grew more and more in love, and sang:

"Oh, man of the world of mortal men, I've lost my heart to thee!"

And that's how it was until the sister of a grocer moved to town.

Her name was Julin, and she was beautiful and clever and it wasn't long before she decided that she would marry Ben. None of the other girls stood a chance beside her and the wedding was soon announced.

When the nymph Mileena heard about the wedding, she cried and raged and sank ships, drowning men who never knew why. But though she hated and loathed, Mileena could not bring herself to despise Ben. She kept her wrath from him. It was Julin for whom she held her anger.

If ever Julin set foot upon a boat, the nymph swore, she would wash that ship out to sea and there torture the woman with storms and bleaching sunlight until her life was shriveled up and gone. She swore it and dreamed it and writhed in her hatred, but Julin didn't know so didn't care, and since she never went aboard ships, (boats were such awful, *dirty* things, she'd say), Mileena was unable to do a thing. The nymph could only go mad to think of Julin standing smug and self satisfied at Ben's side.

Time passed and Julin decided that she would be a mother. Soon after she became pregnant. The rounder she got, the more smug and self satisfied she became and Ben ran to and fro to please her. When Mileena learned of the coming child, it made her insane with jealousy.

The baby was born, and her mother decided to name her Sara, but the child's eyes sparkled like her father's, and as she grew, it became clear that she shared Ben's enchantment.

Sara was quick and bright and strong, and the people lost their hearts to her at once. She had the magic of her father, and the will of her mother, and in this she was a sight! Ben loved her, but Julin fought bitterly with the girl. —Julin was used to people doing as they were told, but Sara only did what suited her. She disobeyed and always with results that made people cry, "How clever! How wonderful! How splendid Sara is!"

Julin spent much of her motherhood livid with frustration, and it only got worse when Sara decided that she wanted to become a sailor like her father.

Mileena frowned on this; Sara was the daughter of the woman she hated most, so she tried her best to make things difficult for the girl. She made the waves choppy and she sent the coldest water up from the ocean floor and several times knocked Sara into the sea. She considered even drowning her out of spite, but decided against it, for fear of breaking Ben's heart, for she knew he loved the girl.

—But even through all of this, Sara shone. She braved the coldest waters and swam like a fish, and indeed, learned to sail better even than her father. Even Mileena found herself grudgingly impressed, but refused to lose her heart to the girl. "Perhaps if she were *my* daughter. But she isn't and I do not like her one bit!"

Julin was upset as well, but for different reasons. She looked between herself and Ben, and then at Sara who didn't want to be like her, and she said, "No daughter of mine. . !"

Mileena laughed at this, and began to favor Sara just because it made the girl's mother hurt inside. She used her will to make sure that Sara was successful in all she did upon the water. —This, when added to Sara's enchantment made the girl seem all the more divine. People marveled at her and adored her, and Sara adored them back.

When the time came for Sara to choose a star, she picked out Mileena's, doing so in all the honesty of youth. She meant her best and hoped that Mileena would love her. The nymph only snorted.

Now when all this came about, Julin complained bitterly, which was nothing new. What *was* new, however, was that on the very night of her daughter's ceremony, she looked upon her own star and made many bitter wishes. Girls were supposed to choose their mother's stars, *not* their father's.

"Something must be done!" she said.

The nymph whose star she wished upon was named Auril, and she agreed, but not for the reasons Julin thought were important, and at first, not even for reasons Auril understood herself.

The nymph Auril worried and wondered but she could not see clearly what made things feel wrong. "Ben and Sara, Ben and Sara," she said to herself. "Why does that ring false?" She decided that she would watch, and it was not long before she spied Ben and his daughter returning home one day from the ocean. She saw Ben's deft hands, and she saw his hair blowing in the wind, and she saw how gaily Sara sprang to shore, and how the boat was filled with the beautiful fish Mileena had sent them. She saw all of these things and understood, exclaiming. "Ah, but what is *this? This* cannot be! But these are two with *Faerie* blood in them, here among the world of mortal kind! This cannot be! This cannot be!" And with that, she sent the nets flying into the air so that they spun about Ben's head and snapped his neck.

Ben's spirit flew up into the air and Auril caught it, telling him, "Dear Ben, you are not supposed to be here. You must come away to where you belong. And your daughter must come too."

Auril would have taken Sara then as well, but Mileena came to stop her, crying, "No, Auril! What are you doing? These two are *mine*. I forbid you!"

But Auril turned upon her, saying, "Mileena, you should know better. These are not for you. They may have chosen so, but they must come away. I must take them back to the borders of Nove, where their kind live."

But the water nymph shook her head, seeing only that Julin had sent Auril to hurt her.

"No!" She cried. "You cannot! You *must* not! They are mine!"

She could do nothing, though; Ben was already gone, and Sara stood upon dry land. All she could do was look up through the waves in rage.

"Foolish girl!" she cried at Sara. "Foolish girl! You swore yourself to me! Come to me at once! Come into the *water!"*

But Sara was stricken with fear, and she did not move.

"Oh, *Mileena!*" Auril sighed.

Mileena only hissed and vanished beneath the brine.

Auril was sorry she had struck Ben dead so abruptly as she had done, and turned to poor Sara, who understood little of what had happened.

"Sara Blue, Sara Blue," she said, her words rising in halos, "I must take you away. I will reach down for you at dusk. You will stand upon your balcony and wait for me. You must bid your mother and your friends good-bye, but then I must take you away."

And with that she flew off into the sky.

Stricken by this news, the fishermen all wept as they made their way back to Sara's home. They came up the hill, a sorry parade for all to see, and everybody felt their heart strings ache. The gossips were quiet and sober as they passed the news to all the ears that cared to hear.

Sara made her good-byes as best she could, and all the people who loved her dressed her up and brought flowers for her hair, saying that Sara must look her best, though really they just didn't know what else they ought to do. Julin scowled into the white of her daughter's dress as she tied the ribbons, hiding her tears from the girl. Sara hugged her anyway, and Julin cried openly, saying that she was so very sorry, though she could not have said exactly what she was sorry for. At dusk, young Sara stood bravely upon her balcony, shifting her bare feet while she watched the sky. It was then that Mileena struck.

Up through the sewers and cracks the water came; a thousand icy wet fingers clutching at the stone. Even as Auril swept down to take Sara, the sea crashed in upon the city with all its pounding might. None is stronger than the sea, and thus Mileena caught Sara away from Auril as she might have snatched a doll.

All the people of Highborn at Oceansend cried out as half their city crumbled and vanished beneath the black water. Mileena held Sara there, and she did not let her go until all the air ran out of the girl's lungs and she died.

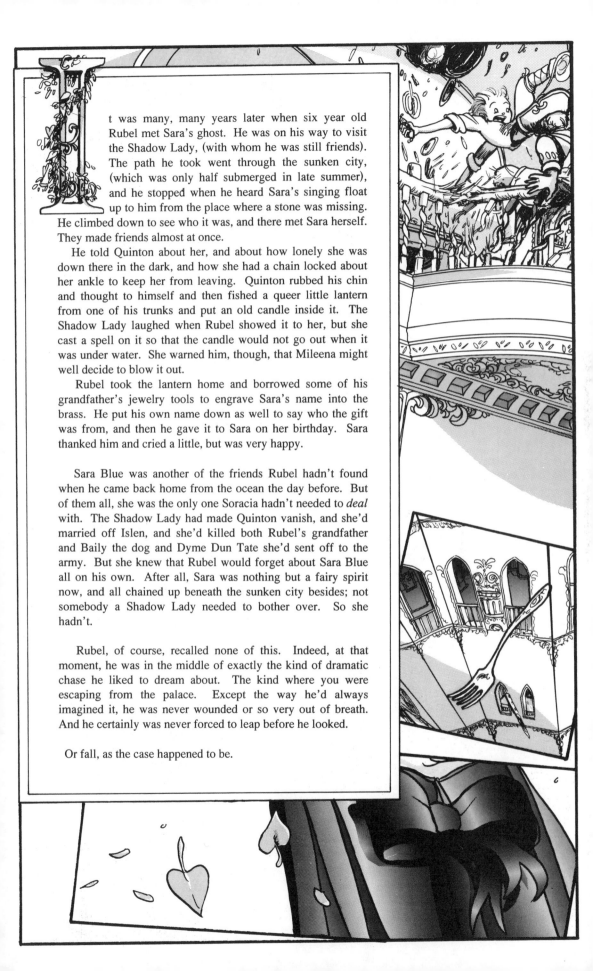

It was many, many years later when six year old Rubel met Sara's ghost. He was on his way to visit the Shadow Lady, (with whom he was still friends). The path he took went through the sunken city, (which was only half submerged in late summer), and he stopped when he heard Sara's singing float up to him from the place where a stone was missing. He climbed down to see who it was, and there met Sara herself. They made friends almost at once.

He told Quinton about her, and about how lonely she was down there in the dark, and how she had a chain locked about her ankle to keep her from leaving. Quinton rubbed his chin and thought to himself and then fished a queer little lantern from one of his trunks and put an old candle inside it. The Shadow Lady laughed when Rubel showed it to her, but she cast a spell on it so that the candle would not go out when it was under water. She warned him, though, that Mileena might well decide to blow it out.

Rubel took the lantern home and borrowed some of his grandfather's jewelry tools to engrave Sara's name into the brass. He put his own name down as well to say who the gift was from, and then he gave it to Sara on her birthday. Sara thanked him and cried a little, but was very happy.

Sara Blue was another of the friends Rubel hadn't found when he came back home from the ocean the day before. But of them all, she was the only one Soracia hadn't needed to *deal* with. The Shadow Lady had made Quinton vanish, and she'd married off Islen, and she'd killed both Rubel's grandfather and Baily the dog and Dyme Dun Tate she'd sent off to the army. But she knew that Rubel would forget about Sara Blue all on his own. After all, Sara was nothing but a fairy spirit now, and all chained up beneath the sunken city besides; not somebody a Shadow Lady needed to bother over. So she hadn't.

Rubel, of course, recalled none of this. Indeed, at that moment, he was in the middle of exactly the kind of dramatic chase he liked to dream about. The kind where you were escaping from the palace. Except the way he'd always imagined it, he was never wounded or so very out of breath. And he certainly was never forced to leap before he looked.

Or fall, as the case happened to be.

Chapter 6

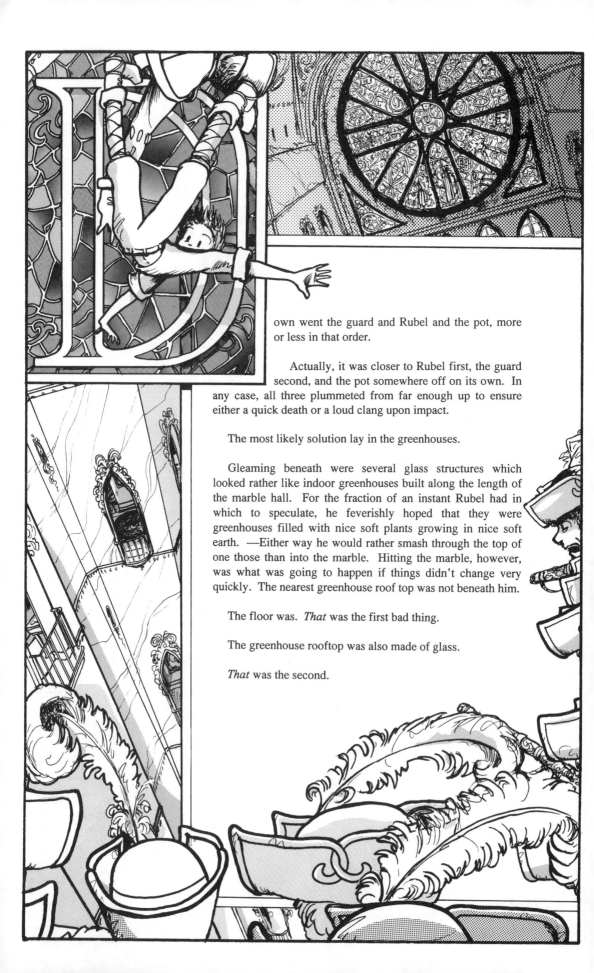

own went the guard and Rubel and the pot, more or less in that order.

Actually, it was closer to Rubel first, the guard second, and the pot somewhere off on its own. In any case, all three plummeted from far enough up to ensure either a quick death or a loud clang upon impact.

The most likely solution lay in the greenhouses.

Gleaming beneath were several glass structures which looked rather like indoor greenhouses built along the length of the marble hall. For the fraction of an instant Rubel had in which to speculate, he feverishly hoped that they were greenhouses filled with nice soft plants growing in nice soft earth. —Either way he would rather smash through the top of one those than into the marble. Hitting the marble, however, was what was going to happen if things didn't change very quickly. The nearest greenhouse roof top was not beneath him.

The floor was. *That* was the first bad thing.

The greenhouse rooftop was also made of glass.

That was the second.

o smash through glass, Rubel knew, was one of the
very worst things that could happen to you. When
he was young, Elly Marth from up the road had
accidentally put her arm through a window pane.
He didn't actually see the accident, but when his
grandfather came back from bringing the doctor, he told Rubel
about it. It was a very bad accident; his grandfather's expression
had been very grim. Elly Marth had cut herself to the white of the
bone, he said; to the *quick*. She would certainly have bled to death
if the doctor hadn't come, and even then her hand would never work
properly again.

This story disturbed Rubel deeply, and he shivered whenever he
saw Elly Marth and caught a glimpse of the ugly scar running from
her wrist to elbow.

Being a thief, however, meant that jumping through windows
was a matter of course; something you just had to put up with, so he
did. Rubel did his best, however, to make sure that he only jumped
through windows if it was absolutely necessary, and only then if he
was reasonably sure that the window would open with him instead
of breaking. The panes of glass below, however, weren't the sort
which opened up at all. They were just plain glass.

But the way around *that* problem, he saw, was falling only a
short distance away from him. Directly above the greenhouse. The
big metal pot. With a big metal pot, he could kill two birds with
one stone.

That is, he (one thief), tucked inside a big metal pot could safely
go through several panes of glass. Like a stone. Or something like
that. It hardly mattered at this speed. Rubel clambered up the
howling guard and jumped off him.

With both hands grasping through space, Rubel seized the pot
and only just managed to half cram himself inside before it struck.
The guardsman roared into the floor with a merciless 'Smat' and the
pot, with Rubel inside it, burst through the greenhouse roof in a
spectacular cloud of shattered glass and splintered wood, throwing
the tropical birds into a flurry of feathers and terrified squawks
amongst all the exotic plants and fruit trees.

The only problem was that there were no exotic plants or fruit
trees. And the birds weren't tropical. They were pigeons. And the
greenhouse windows weren't really greenhouse windows at all.
They were observation windows.

Indeed, it struck Rubel at this moment that he had never
heard of such a thing as an indoor greenhouse before.

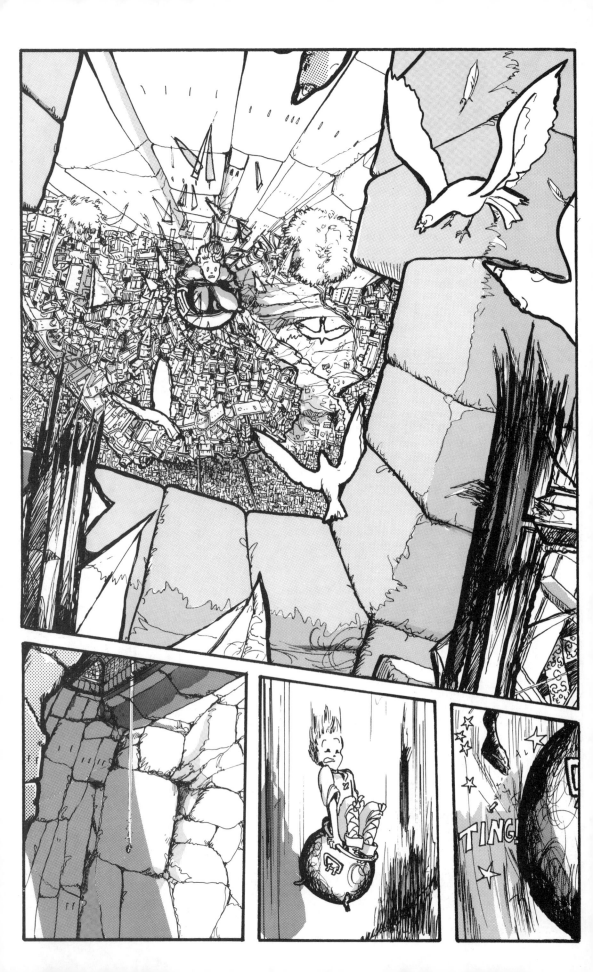

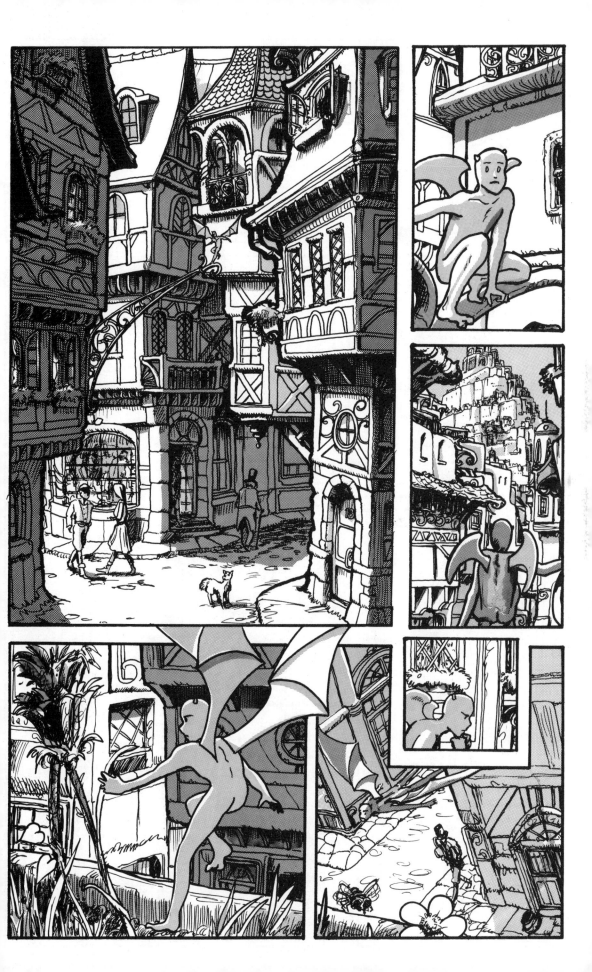

RUBEL?

I SAW A TRAIL OF **BLOOD** COMING HERE.

YOU'RE BLEEDING?

YEAH

THERE YOU ARE!

WHAT HAPPENED?

OH WOW,

WAS IT THE SHADOW LADY?

IT WAS HER, RIGHT? —I KNOW 'CAUSE SHE USED MAGIC ON ME AGAIN, AND I HEARD HER VOICE!

YEAH.

IT WAS HER.

CAN I SEE WHERE YOU GOT HURT?

IS IT BAD?

GAH! RIGHT IN YOUR STOMACH!

HOW'D IT HAPPEN?

I DUNNO. I GOT SHOT I GUESS.

YEAH...

OH WOW. IT'S *REALLY* IN THERE!

DOES IT HURT?

A BIT.

MOSTLY JUST WHEN I TRY TO MOVE IT.

ARE YOU GOING TO PULL IT OUT?

I CAN'T DECIDE.

I GUESS I SHOULD, BUT EACH TIME I TRY, I GET ALL DIZZY AND I START SMELLING FLOWERS.

FLOWERS?

OH *WOW!*

I KNOW WHAT THAT MEANS!

IT PROBABLY MEANS THERE WAS *POISON* ON THE TIP!

YEAH.

AND IT WAS THE *SHADOW LADY*, RIGHT?

SHE'S THE ONE WHO DID IT?

YES.

AND I DON'T THINK IT WAS JUST REGULAR POISON EITHER.

IT'S DOING SOMETHING ELSE TO ME AS WELL...

MAGIC POISON?

OH *WOW.*

WHAT ARE YOU GOING TO DO?

I DON'T KNOW.

WELL, I CAN'T LEAVE IT *IN*.

I STARTED TO FEEL SICK BEFORE YOU GOT HERE, AND THE FLOWERS KEEP GETTING STRONGER.

IT'S THE POISON...

SHE'S PROBABLY WAITING UNTIL IT TAKES FULL EFFECT ON ME, AND THEN SHE'LL COME DOWN AND OFFER ME AN ANTIDOTE IN EXCHANGE FOR MY **SOUL**.

YOUR SOUL! YOU THINK SO?

YEAH.

OR SOMETHING LIKE THAT. —AND I THINK SHE PUT A SPELL ON THE BOLT TOO. —TO MAKE IT HARD FOR ME TO PULL OUT.

THAT'S WHY I GET DIZZY WHEN I TOUCH IT, AND WHY IT DOESN'T HURT WHEN I LEAVE IT ALONE.

SO YOU SHOULD PULL IT OUT THEN!

IF THAT'S WHAT IT IS, YOU SHOULD PULL IT OUT RIGHT AWAY!

HMM...

NO...

WHAT I DO IS...

YEAH!

YEAH, WHAT I DO IS AFTER I PULL IT OUT, I STAB HER WITH IT.

WITH THE SAME BOLT SHE SHOT ME WITH!

THEN SHE'LL BE POISONED TOO!

HEY...

THAT'S NOT BAD...

YEAH!

THEN SHE'LL ALSO NEED THE ANTIDOTE!

AND WHEN SHE TAKES IT OUT TO USE IT, I CAN FLY UP AND STEAL IT FROM HER!

THEN SHE'LL HAVE TO DO WHAT WE SAY!

WOW!

WHAT A GREAT PLAN!

AND TO MAKE IT SO THE ARROW HEAD WILL GO INTO HER, WHAT I DO IS TAKE THE LOCK OF HAIR PRINCESS KATARA GAVE TO ME, AND TIE IT TO THE POINT!

EXCUSE ME?

REMEMBER..? ONLY THREE THINGS IN THE WORLD CAN MAKE THE SHADOW LADY BLEED.

AND I HAVE ONE OF THEM!

OOOOH, RIGHT...

I FORGOT ABOUT THAT.

WHAT ABOUT WHEN YOU HAVE TO JUMP UP? DO YOU THINK YOU'LL BE ABLE TO DO THAT?

WHAT ABOUT THE SPELL TO MAKE YOU DIZZY?

AND I BET YOU'LL BE BLEEDING A LOT AFTER YOU PULL IT OUT...

NOT IF I PULL IT OUT QUICK AND ALL AT ONCE.

QUINTON TOLD ME HOW ONCE.

QUINTON DID..?

YEAH. YOU GIVE IT A HARD TWIST AND SORT OF YANK IT BOTH AT THE SAME TIME.

THAT MAKES THE WOUND SWELL UP AND CLOSE OFF THE BLEEDING. —IT HEALS FASTER.

IT DOES? YEAH.

AND THE EXTRA PAIN MAKES YOU MORE ALERT.

THAT WAY I'LL BE ABLE TO ACT MORE ASSERTIVELY WHEN SHE GETS HERE.

IT SHOULD COUNTER-ACT THE DIZZY SPELL!

I GUESS...

BUT AREN'T YOU SUPPOSED TO BE MORE GENTLE WHEN YOU PULL OUT ARROWS?

NO.

THAT'S JUST A POPULAR MISCONCEPTION. —IT'S ONE OF THOSE IDEAS THAT WORKS BACKWARDS.

QUINTON TOLD ME THIS STORY ABOUT A GUY NAMED 'JAQUES QUICK' AND HOW HE DID IT.

 "JAQUES *QUICK?*"

 HE WAS A SOLDIER.

 HE WAS WOUNDED IN THE MIDDLE OF A BATTLE AND HAD TO PULL AN ARROW FROM HIS STOMACH.

 YEAH, EXCEPT QUINTON'S KIND OF AN IDIOT.

NO HE'S *NOT*

 HE'S JUST GOT AN UNCONVENTIONAL MIND. —REGULAR PEOPLE DON'T UNDERSTAND THINGS THE WAY HE DOES.

THAT'S WHAT I MEAN.

 OH RELAX! IT'LL BE FINE!

I'M SURE HE KNOWS WHAT HE'S TALKING ABOUT.

IF YOU SAY SO...

I DO. QUINTON *NEVER* SAYS THINGS WITHOUT A *GOOD* REASON.

 NOW, I HAVE TO *CONCENTRATE,* SO BE QUIET, OKAY.

OKAY.

 ONE.., TWO..,

 SHLUCK

 AUGHHHH!

 RUBEL!

Chapter 7

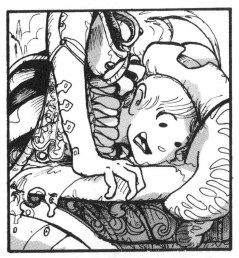

CAREFUL.

I EXPECT IT
HAS TEETH.

PLOOP!

I SAT IN A TREE AND JUST STARED AT IT FROM ACROSS THE BATTLE-FIELD. —THE COLORS WERE *SO* *VIVID*. —AND. IT LOOKED *JUST* LIKE HER, EXCEPT IN SWIRLS AND WHATNOT.

IT WAS *SO* BEAUTIFUL.

IT MADE *ME* WANT TO DO A PAINTING AS WELL.

DID YOU?

WELL, I TRIED, BUT I COULDN'T GET THE PAINTS TO WORK.

MY COLORS TURNED ALL BROWN AND YUCKY.

I USED THE SAME PLANTS AND ROOTS AND EVERYTHING, BUT THEY JUST WOULDN'T WORK.

—I SPENT A WHOLE YEAR TRYING!

—WELL, IT WAS LATER, BECAUSE THE WAR WAS ON.

BUT A *WHOLE* YEAR!

EVENTUALLY I GAVE UP AND WENT AND GOT *REAL* PAINT; THE KIND YOU *BUY*.

BUT I COULDN'T USE *THOSE* EITHER.

IF I WAS BAD AT MIXING PAINTS, THEN I WAS EVEN WORSE AT USING THEM.

I GUESS THAT MAKES SENSE.

PAINTING IS VERY DIFFICULT. —MORE DIFFICULT THAN MIXING.

I CAN'T PAINT EITHER.

BUT IT SHOULDN'T BE THAT WAY FOR *ME*!

I HAD A HUNDRED YEARS TO PRACTICE! BUT MY PICTURES ALL TURNED OUT UGLY AND HORRIBLE. —AND I TRIED *SO* HARD. I MUST HAVE FILLED.., *FIVE* THOUSAND CANVASES... —*TEN* THOUSAND!

AND I DIDN'T EVEN COME *CLOSE*. —IN THE END, I WAS PRACTICALLY IN TEARS I WAS SO FURIOUS. I HUNTED HIM DOWN AND DEMANDED TO KNOW HOW LONG HE'D HAD TO PRACTICE, OR WHAT KIND OF MAGIC HE'D USED... I WAS TERRIFIED OF DOING *THAT*!

I KNEW DEEP INSIDE WHAT HIS ANSWER WAS GOING TO BE, BUT I COULDN'T STOP MYSELF.

WHAT DO YOU MEAN?

I MEAN...

YOU FORGIVE PEOPLE VERY EASILY.

YOU ALWAYS FORGAVE ME WHEN YOU WERE SMALL.

I FORGAVE YOU?

YES.

I WAS ALWAYS SO MEAN AND SCARY, BUT YOU KEPT COMING TO VISIT ME ANYWAY.

IN THE FOREST.

REMEMBER?

SORT OF...

I WAS ONE OF YOUR FRIENDS.

AND I NEVER MADE YOU COME.

NOT ONCE.

YOU VISITED BECAUSE YOU WANTED TO.

REMEMBER?

I GUESS SO.

...

IT'S OKAY IF YOU DON'T.

NO.

NO. I THINK I DO REMEMBER.

I MEAN, I REMEMBER YOU, BUT I ALSO THINK I REMEMBER SOMETHING LIKE THAT...

DID I EVER BRING YOU A LITTLE BRASS LANTERN?

YES.

I PUT A SPELL ON THE CANDLE INSIDE.

YES! THAT WAS ME!

Chapter 8

Panel 1:

I'VE GOT THE ROPES!

WILLIAM, I NEED YOU IN THAT TREE TO HELP WITH THE PULLEYS!

AYE, AYE, YOUR ROYAL WIZARDNESS!

SHOULD I TAKE **EXTRA** CARE?

FLICK

Panel 2:

NATURALLY. —YOU MUSTN'T SLIP.

WE HAVE NO TIME TO WASTE ON PERSONAL INJURIES.

DOES MR. VANDERKOFF EVEN KNOW YOU TOOK HIS WINE PRESS, QUINTON?

Panel 3:

I HOPE NOT.

YOU KNOW HOW THAT MAN IS IN WEATHER LIKE THIS.

IN WEATHER LIKE THIS? BUT HE'S **ALWAYS** MAD AT YOU.

Panel 4:

IT'S THE GENERAL AIR PRESSURE AT THIS ALTITUDE.

SQUEEZES THE BRAIN.

I'VE ADVISED HIM MORE THAN ONCE TO MOVE CLOSER TO THE MOUNTAINS, —WITH A CRANIUM LIKE HIS, THERE'S NO TELLING WHAT HE'S LIABLE TO DO.

Panel 5:

I THINK HE GETS MAD BECAUSE YOU ALWAYS TAKE HIS STUFF WITHOUT ASKING.

NONSENSE!

ANY STOUT-HEARTED CITIZEN WOULD BE MORE THAN WILLING TO DO HIS PART!

BUT EACH TIME I ASK HIM, VANDERKOFF STARTS **SHOOTING** AT ME!

THE MAN'S A MENACE!

Panel 6:

YOU SIMPLY CAN'T TELL A GUY LIKE VANDERKOFF UP FRONT THAT YOU'RE TAKING HIS STUFF.

—IT'S FAR SAFER TO LET HIM FIND OUT ONCE YOU'VE GOTTEN AWAY.

BOY!

MR. VANDERKOFF WILL SURE BE MAD WHEN HE FINDS OUT! —I BET YOU'LL HAVE TO PULL WEEDS AGAIN!

QUINTON. WHAT'S GOING ON?

IT DOESN'T MEAN THAT IF YOU DON'T SAY IT TO HIM, DOES IT?

I NEVER SAID IT TO HIM.

HUM! —I THINK HEATH'S IN LOVE WITH HIM!

YOU GOT A CRUSH ON QUINTON, HEATH?

NO I DON'T!

WE'RE JUST FRIENDS.

BUT HE'S A CRAZY GUY! —YOU'RE FRIENDS WITH A CRAZY GUY?

HE'S NOT CRAZY!

AND YOU GUYS ARE JERKS FOR TRYING TO GET HIM IN TROUBLE!

HE NEVER DID ANYTHING TO YOU!

OOOH BOO HOO!

BUT WE'RE NOT TRYING TO GET HIM IN TROUBLE. —WE'RE JUST GOING ALONG WITH HIM.

YEAH. IT'S NOT AS IF WE COULD STOP HIM. —AND ANYWAY, MY DAD SAYS IT'S WRONG TO STOP PEOPLE FROM FOLLOWIN' THEIR OWN INTERESTS NO MATTER WHAT THEY MIGHT DAMN-WELL BE.

SO WHERE'S THE HARM IN GOING ALONG?

I MEAN, IF HE'S NOT CRAZY, LIKE YOU SAY?

. . .

THAT'S RIGHT!

I MEAN, THERE'S NOTHING WRONG UNLESS MAYBE HE REALLY IS CRAZY.

IT'S THE CRAZY PEOPLE WHO GIVE REGULAR FOLKS LIKE MY DAD A BAD NAME! —THAT'S WHAT MY DAD SAYS.

WHAT DO YOU THINK, HEATH? —MAYBE QUINTON IS NUTS, AND YOU JUST DON'T WANT ANYONE TO KNOW 'CAUSE YOU LIKE HIM SO MUCH.

THAT'S NOT IT!

uinton was, without question, the most extraordinary adult Heath had ever known, but try as she might, she just couldn't tell if he was really a wizard. —The *instinctive* part of her certainly believed. Her instinctive part believed at once and without question. But the *rest* of her. . .

It was difficult to face the William Furloffs of the world when all you had were your instincts.

Certainly, there weren't very many reasons she *should* believe. Quinton had never once performed magic in front of her. Not even a small piece. (Indeed, it occurred to her that neither she nor anybody else had ever actually *demanded* Quinton do anything to prove himself. It occurred to her as well, that each time she resolved to ask, the thought somehow always managed to forget itself. Good opportunities were never present, and generally, whatever adventures Quinton happened to be involved with soon swept you up as well so that you forgot entirely about other things. This in itself seemed like magic of a sort, and Heath felt quite clever when she thought of it. But still, it was hardly enough. William would just laugh).

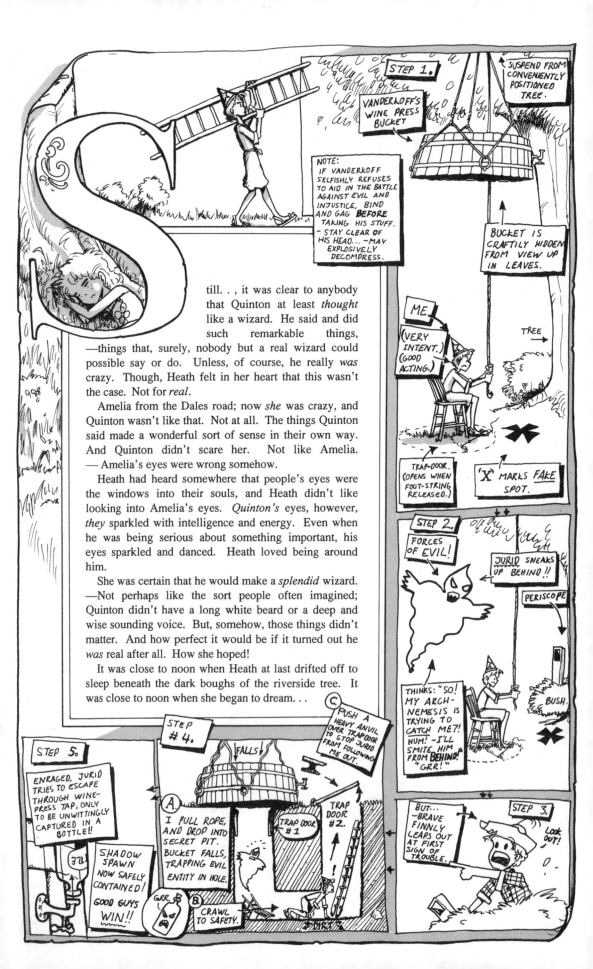

till. . , it was clear to anybody that Quinton at least *thought* like a wizard. He said and did such remarkable things, —things that, surely, nobody but a real wizard could possible say or do. Unless, of course, he really *was* crazy. Though, Heath felt in her heart that this wasn't the case. Not for *real*.

Amelia from the Dales road; now *she* was crazy, and Quinton wasn't like that. Not at all. The things Quinton said made a wonderful sort of sense in their own way. And Quinton didn't scare her. Not like Amelia. — Amelia's eyes were wrong somehow.

Heath had heard somewhere that people's eyes were the windows into their souls, and Heath didn't like looking into Amelia's eyes. *Quinton's* eyes, however, *they* sparkled with intelligence and energy. Even when he was being serious about something important, his eyes sparkled and danced. Heath loved being around him.

She was certain that he would make a *splendid* wizard. —Not perhaps like the sort people often imagined; Quinton didn't have a long white beard or a deep and wise sounding voice. But, somehow, those things didn't matter. And how perfect it would be if it turned out he *was* real after all. How she hoped!

It was close to noon when Heath at last drifted off to sleep beneath the dark boughs of the riverside tree. It was close to noon when she began to dream. . .

She dreamed in the warm darkness which lay behind her eyelids. And in the cooler, moist darkness when she nudged sideways into the grass. The rich smell of earth surrounded her, and she sank further into the inky depths of sleep which lay beyond.

"Your eyes shut. Your mouth shut." a voice instructed. The words echoed from far, far off. Dire and hurried, but also very sure.

It was a woman's voice.

"Hm!" somebody answered through the darkness. "I don't like this. Not one bit!"

"Shut," the woman repeated.

Heath snapped alert to sound of the two voices, finding herself surrounded by a dark that was thicker than night. —Like the inside of a sealed closet, but somehow even darker than that.

'What is this now?' she asked in her mind, 'I heard somebody! I think I must be inside a cave!'

She took a step forward and her shoes scuffed and missed on the stone, very nearly pitching her into the blackness.

With arms flung out, she steadied herself. The earth seemed to spin ponderously beneath her, as though it were not quite sure of itself. Clutching and swallowing, she went ridged until the motion settled and stopped.

'This won't do!' she thought, straining her eyes into the darkness. 'I can't see a thing! What sort of dream is this? I've dreamed in all sorts of places before, but I've always been able to see at least *something!*'

Then, as though in silent answer, her surroundings quietly swam into view. The stones paused and shifted just beyond her perception, as though waiting for their forms to be fully decided before materializing through the shadows. She knew for certain then that she was in a dream.

"But this is still very different from anything I've ever dreamed before!" she said to herself, speaking aloud the way people sometimes do when they are trying not to be afraid.

What was that?" came the boy's voice again, closer now. "Did you hear that?"

"You mustn't listen!" the woman answered. "You don't understand how dangerous this is! If you let yourself hear things, then the labyrinth is only a heartbeat away from seizing you! Quickly, we must keep moving!"

"Let myself. . ? But I can't help what I hear!"

"You can. You must. This is the very heart of Rogue's slumber. This is where the very deepest of the Dragon's sleep draws its power. You sense how the stones shift beneath you? Even *they* wonder if they are real in the face of this."

"Was there somebody there?"

"I don't know! —And you must not *try* to know. Don't ask such questions. —Rubel! You are not heeding a single thing I say! I know it is in your nature, but you must believe me when I tell you that you are tempting great peril! The darkest corners of your soul can flow freely here if you are not careful. They will be drawn out to share in this; out through your mouth and ears and nose! Pinch them closed. Your nightmares, Rubel. The deepest fears within your soul; even a thief must be wary! The only way to pass safely is to push forward and not turn left or right until we see the light. —And wondering upon your fears, and thinking upon the knots tied within you, —that is left and right, Rubel! Now hold your tongue and hold my hand tightly; even *I* must step with care here, and I am a master of such things as these!"

Heath could hear them very near now. They were coming closer and her heart raced faster as they did. He was real! —She realized this at once, and the force of it struck her like a mountain.

Her first lesson was today.

A shiver ran down her body and she was galvanized with sudden implications as they struck. She took a step forward, filled with a breathtaking sensation; powerful *certainty*.

She was *supposed* to be here.

Nothing was wrong at all! She was *going* to become a sorceress. A *real* one. Quinton hadn't forgotten his promise to her at all! He had *planned* it this way!

The feeling was exquisite; As though all the pieces to a difficult puzzle had suddenly fallen into place; solved before her eyes like. . .

Magic.

The William Furloffs and their loud mouth brothers of the world faded from significance next to this. But there was something even more. . .

Heath was aware of something stirring within her. It lulled her forward, causing the enchantment within her to grow until it blazed like a *sun*.

And then, they were before her.

All of them.

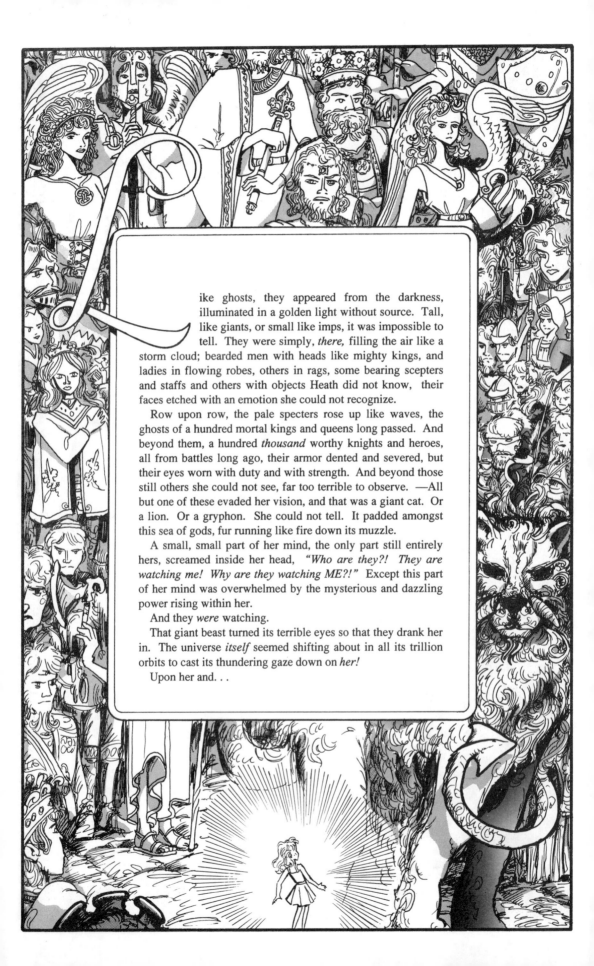

ike ghosts, they appeared from the darkness, illuminated in a golden light without source. Tall, like giants, or small like imps, it was impossible to tell. They were simply, *there,* filling the air like a storm cloud; bearded men with heads like mighty kings, and ladies in flowing robes, others in rags, some bearing scepters and staffs and others with objects Heath did not know, their faces etched with an emotion she could not recognize.

Row upon row, the pale specters rose up like waves, the ghosts of a hundred mortal kings and queens long passed. And beyond them, a hundred *thousand* worthy knights and heroes, all from battles long ago, their armor dented and severed, but their eyes worn with duty and with strength. And beyond those still others she could not see, far too terrible to observe. —All but one of these evaded her vision, and that was a giant cat. Or a lion. Or a gryphon. She could not tell. It padded amongst this sea of gods, fur running like fire down its muzzle.

A small, small part of her mind, the only part still entirely hers, screamed inside her head, *"Who are they?! They are watching me! Why are they watching ME?!"* Except this part of her mind was overwhelmed by the mysterious and dazzling power rising within her.

And they *were* watching.

That giant beast turned its terrible eyes so that they drank her in. The universe *itself* seemed shifting about in all its trillion orbits to cast its thundering gaze down on *her!*

Upon her and. . .

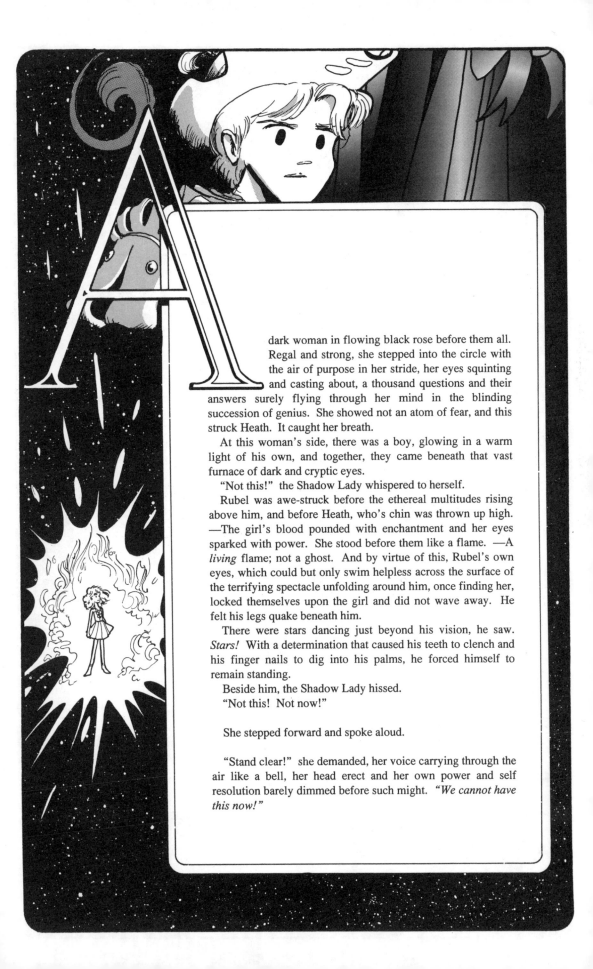

A dark woman in flowing black rose before them all. Regal and strong, she stepped into the circle with the air of purpose in her stride, her eyes squinting and casting about, a thousand questions and their answers surely flying through her mind in the blinding succession of genius. She showed not an atom of fear, and this struck Heath. It caught her breath.

At this woman's side, there was a boy, glowing in a warm light of his own, and together, they came beneath that vast furnace of dark and cryptic eyes.

"Not this!" the Shadow Lady whispered to herself.

Rubel was awe-struck before the ethereal multitudes rising above him, and before Heath, who's chin was thrown up high. —The girl's blood pounded with enchantment and her eyes sparked with power. She stood before them like a flame. —A *living* flame; not a ghost. And by virtue of this, Rubel's own eyes, which could but only swim helpless across the surface of the terrifying spectacle unfolding around him, once finding her, locked themselves upon the girl and did not wave away. He felt his legs quake beneath him.

There were stars dancing just beyond his vision, he saw. *Stars!* With a determination that caused his teeth to clench and his finger nails to dig into his palms, he forced himself to remain standing.

Beside him, the Shadow Lady hissed.

"Not this! Not now!"

She stepped forward and spoke aloud.

"Stand clear!" she demanded, her voice carrying through the air like a bell, her head erect and her own power and self resolution barely dimmed before such might. *"We cannot have this now!"*

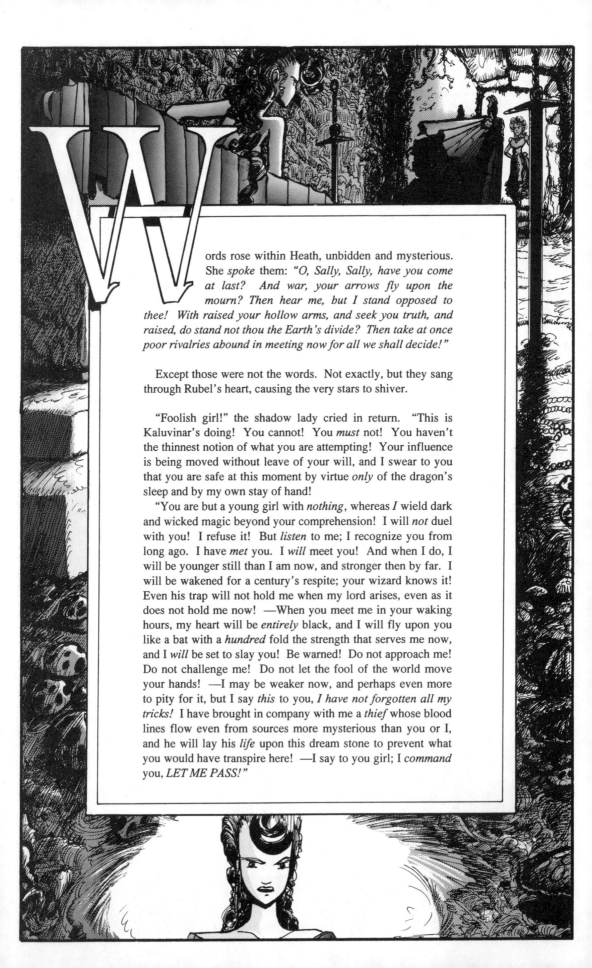

ords rose within Heath, unbidden and mysterious. She *spoke* them: *"O, Sally, Sally, have you come at last? And war, your arrows fly upon the mourn? Then hear me, but I stand opposed to thee! With raised your hollow arms, and seek you truth, and raised, do stand not thou the Earth's divide? Then take at once poor rivalries abound in meeting now for all we shall decide!"*

Except those were not the words. Not exactly, but they sang through Rubel's heart, causing the very stars to shiver.

"Foolish girl!" the shadow lady cried in return. "This is Kaluvinar's doing! You cannot! You *must* not! You haven't the thinnest notion of what you are attempting! Your influence is being moved without leave of your will, and I swear to you that you are safe at this moment by virtue *only* of the dragon's sleep and by my own stay of hand!

"You are but a young girl with *nothing*, whereas *I* wield dark and wicked magic beyond your comprehension! I will *not* duel with you! I refuse it! But *listen* to me; I recognize you from long ago. I have *met* you. I *will* meet you! And when I do, I will be younger still than I am now, and stronger then by far. I will be wakened for a century's respite; your wizard knows it! Even his trap will not hold me when my lord arises, even as it does not hold me now! —When you meet me in your waking hours, my heart will be *entirely* black, and I will fly upon you like a bat with a *hundred* fold the strength that serves me now, and I *will* be set to slay you! Be warned! Do not approach me! Do not challenge me! Do not let the fool of the world move your hands! —I may be weaker now, and perhaps even more to pity for it, but I say *this* to you, *I have not forgotten all my tricks!* I have brought in company with me a *thief* whose blood lines flow even from sources more mysterious than you or I, and he will lay his *life* upon this dream stone to prevent what you would have transpire here! —I say to you girl; I *command* you, *LET ME PASS!"*

Heath felt the power coursing through her body falter ever so slightly, and she realized at once that indeed she did not know what was going on. The thrilling knife edge of perfection she had been so effortlessly balancing on was, in that moment, lost. —And all the attention of the heavens was not such that it would hold itself upon something so faltering as that! It all began to unravel.

Heath cast her eyes about in confusion as the sea of ghosts began to fade, leaving her lost and shaky and frightened. The giant cat roiled its fiery pelt, and with a soft rumble from deep within its throat, slipped into the darkness and was gone. The Shadow Lady and thief faded last of all. Heath watched them as she was lifted up into the dizzy light and humid fragrance of the day.

The boy watched after her, his own chin turned up towards her, his gaze holding hers for one last instant. He stood at the shadow woman's side, his own light shining warm and strong about him. Vital. And then he was gone and the warm air of day filled her lungs sweetly, as though she had been holding her breath the whole time beneath her tree beside the river.

WHAT WAS THAT?!
WHO WAS THAT GIRL?
WHAT HAPPENED?!

WE WERE EXTREMELY LUCKY, IS WHAT HAPPENED!

I WAS A FOOL!

I CAN'T BELIEVE I JUST WALKED INTO THAT!

EITHER HE'S GETTING BETTER, OR I'M GETTING WORSE!

HE HAD ME ON EVERY ANGLE!

I'VE BEEN OUT OF PRACTICE FAR TOO LONG!

WAS THAT PRINCESS KATARA?

NO. NOT PRECISELY.

WHO WAS SHE, THEN? SHE LOOKED LIKE THE PRINCESS.

A BIT DIFFERENT, I GUESS. YOUNGER, BUT...

IT WASN'T HER.

I DON'T HAVE TIME TO EXPLAIN. HURRY!

THERE IT IS! THAT'S THE TEA HOUSE! WE MUST RUN!

WHAT..?!
NO THIEVES ALLOWED!

YOU THERE! HURRY! RUN!

WHAT IS THE MEANING OF THIS?!

King's Crossing

BY DRAGON'S RULE

BEVERAGES FREE TO ROYALTY

NO THIEVES ALLOWED!

Chapter 9

Cespinarve Rogue was a dragon.

He was one of the smaller ones, only about as big as a medium sized mountain range, and perhaps not quite as old as the hills.

Anyway, being something of a runt, the other dragons tended not to take him very seriously. They either teased or ignored him, and otherwise did not make him feel as though he were good enough to be a true part of their important company. And dragons *were* an important company. Dragons, you see, were the keepers of a very serious and ancient task.

long way away from where Rubel lived, there was an extraordinary land called *Nove.* —Although, it wasn't actually *called* Nove anymore. Not since everybody had forgotten the name. These days, the land was called by many other names. *Salisary, Amsil,* and *Troor* were a few of them, and as is the case with most lands, *Earth* was another. None of those names, however, was Nove. Not anymore. Not unless there were dragons around. The *dragons* called it Nove. Dragons were among the oldest living things, and so they remembered.

All the others came later; all the fairies and satyrs and unicorns, and all the other various creatures of myth and legend. —Nove was, in fact, where *most* of the fairy tale creatures, and indeed, where most fairy tales came from; where fairy tales were considered *history,* and not queer stories told to children.

Nove was a long, long way away, and very difficult to get to besides. In fact, so few ever went, that people hardly bothered even *believing* in Nove anymore. Small children, (though they hardly ever asked), were told that it was far off in the north. —You went north, all the way up to the north pole, and once you were there at the top of the world, you traveled north some more until you found it, spread out like a giant magic carpet at your feet. —Which was, of course, ridiculous, and why most people didn't believe anymore.

"After you get to the north pole, you can't go north anymore! The only direction you can go next is *south!* Doesn't matter which way you turn! It's like a ball, see," Adults would tell their children, and feel wise.

Anyway, they were wrong. About Nove being in the north, that is. It was in a much more easterly direction.

It was, in fact, through the sleeping wood. —The sleeping wood against which they had locked their city's eastern doors so long ago. (After the white stones had been broken all to bits.) And that's where the dragons lived. In Nove. Or rather, all around its edges, consuming it the way one might chew a bread crust.

ove was the sort of land which grew. It grew outward from the middle, spreading out larger and wider until, if left alone, it would eventually crumble and fall to pieces.

Rather like a cookie. —A small cookie, you can pick up and hold quite nicely, but a cookie the size of, say, a table top, would just break to pieces if you tried to lift it. Nove was the same way, just on a larger scale. Except when a land like Nove gets too big and starts to break apart, it means having earthquakes and volcanoes going off, and everybody getting dashed to a terrible end. And so it was the dragon's charge to make certain this disaster never befell their world.

Ever since the beginning of time, the dragons stomped and curled around the edges of Nove, eating and munching old hills and mountains and dead forests and used up fields so that things stayed the proper size. It was a very important job and they took it very seriously.

Of course, despite their usefulness, dragons have always had a bad time of it in Nove's historical accounts. As with many expansive systems where people are just a tiny part, folks had trouble comprehending how things actually worked. Just because Nove was always growing, it didn't mean that if you built a house near the middle of the land you would eventually wake up one morning to see your porch falling off into the abyss. (Or down a dragon's gullet.) —Well, it would *eventually*, but it would take a very long time. Your porch would have turned to dust long before then.

The land grew even more slowly than the rivers of solid ice which are glaciers. People simply didn't know the land behaved the way it did. —They didn't know it would crumble apart if not taken care of, and because of this, they didn't understand the dragons. They just heard about dragons from travelers who had journeyed to the edge, and they listened to their stories in fear.

And then, of course, there was Cespinarve Rogue who ate cities. . .

It would be unfair to say that Rogue was the only one. There were the *other* dragons; the small, mortal ones spawned, as much as anything, from simply the *idea* of the original dragons. (The original dragons were so very magical that things like *belief* played a strong part in their very existence. When magic of that sort is about, there will generally be peculiar side effects. That's where the *other* dragons came from). These were the ones which filled the legends of dragons that most people are familiar with. These were the dragons who brooded in caves over piles of treasure, who fought with knights and breathed fire and demanded virgin sacrifices from terrified kingdoms. Mere worms, really, by comparison to a dragon like Rogue. And that was the core of the problem.

Cespinarve Rogue was one of the *first,* and the size of several mountains to boot. This presented a real dilemma. You couldn't send a knight out to slay a dragon like Rogue. Not even a whole legion of knights would be any use. One half hearted snort of flame from his crater sized nostrils, and a whole army would be done for. Broiled to sizzling and then some.

The nature, however, of situations like this is that when powers so awesome and terrible as Rogue rear themselves up in the land, (and especially a land like Nove), *other* powers are roused into being. In this case it was a local figure who had gone otherwise unnoticed till then, (he kept mostly to himself). His name was McGi.

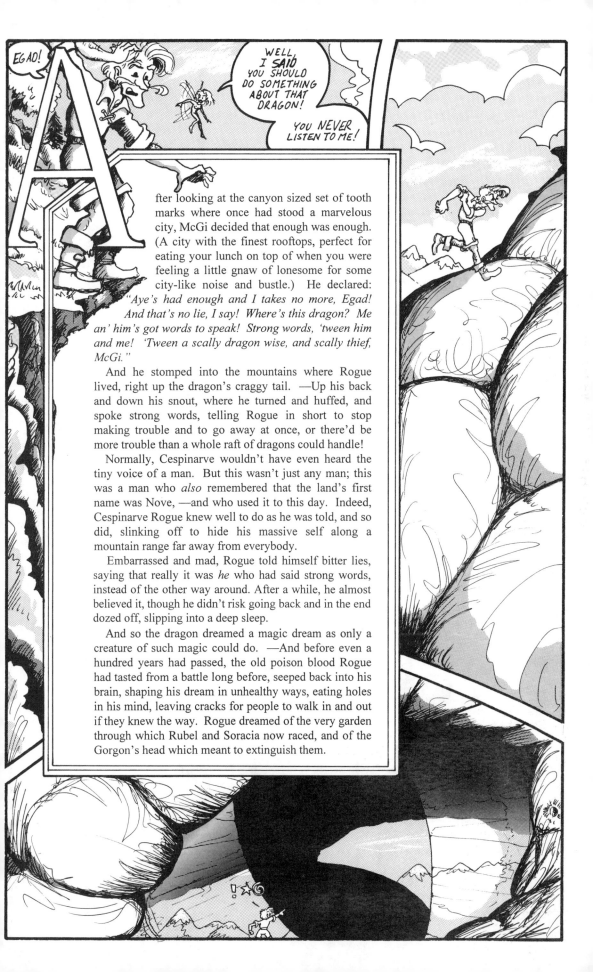

EGAD!

WELL, I **SAID** YOU SHOULD DO SOMETHING ABOUT THAT DRAGON!

YOU NEVER LISTEN TO ME!

After looking at the canyon sized set of tooth marks where once had stood a marvelous city, McGi decided that enough was enough. (A city with the finest rooftops, perfect for eating your lunch on top of when you were feeling a little gnaw of lonesome for some city-like noise and bustle.) He declared:

"Aye's had enough and I takes no more, Egad! And that's no lie, I say! Where's this dragon? Me an' him's got words to speak! Strong words, 'tween him and me! 'Tween a scally dragon wise, and scally thief, McGi."

And he stomped into the mountains where Rogue lived, right up the dragon's craggy tail. —Up his back and down his snout, where he turned and huffed, and spoke strong words, telling Rogue in short to stop making trouble and to go away at once, or there'd be more trouble than a whole raft of dragons could handle!

Normally, Cespinarve wouldn't have even heard the tiny voice of a man. But this wasn't just any man; this was a man who *also* remembered that the land's first name was Nove, —and who used it to this day. Indeed, Cespinarve Rogue knew well to do as he was told, and so did, slinking off to hide his massive self along a mountain range far away from everybody.

Embarrassed and mad, Rogue told himself bitter lies, saying that really it was *he* who had said strong words, instead of the other way around. After a while, he almost believed it, though he didn't risk going back and in the end dozed off, slipping into a deep sleep.

And so the dragon dreamed a magic dream as only a creature of such magic could do. —And before even a hundred years had passed, the old poison blood Rogue had tasted from a battle long before, seeped back into his brain, shaping his dream in unhealthy ways, eating holes in his mind, leaving cracks for people to walk in and out if they knew the way. Rogue dreamed of the very garden through which Rubel and Soracia now raced, and of the Gorgon's head which meant to extinguish them.

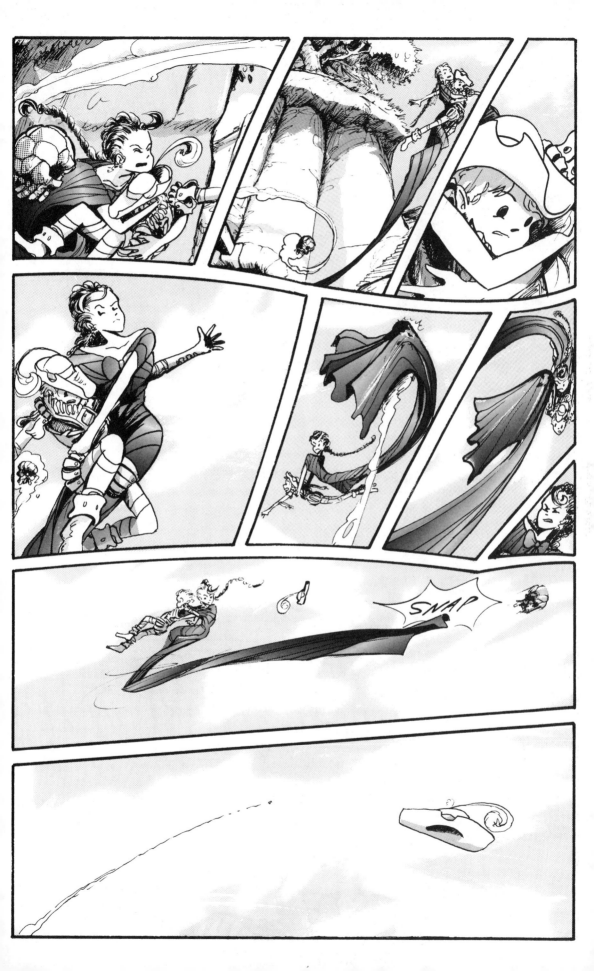

SNAP

ROAR

IS THAT IT?

IS IT GONE?

ARE YOU GOING TO DIE, LIKE YOU SAID, BUT COME BACK AGAIN?

—WHEN WE WAKE UP FROM THIS PLACE?

IT'S SWEET OF YOU TO ASK...

BUT YOU MUST BE WARY OF ME WHEN YOU WAKE.

I WILL BE EVEN WORSE WHEN YOU SEE ME AGAIN, I THINK.

—I DON'T THINK THINGS WILL BE GETTING BETTER.

YES. I'LL BE OKAY.

I'VE DONE THIS BEFORE.

JUST NEVER SO DRAMATICALLY.

MMM...

AM I GOING TO BE OKAY?

I'VE NEVER BEEN HURT LIKE THAT BEFORE.

I KNOW YOU SAID I SHOULDN'T MOVE, BUT I WAS MAD AT YOU...

AND NOW I THINK I'M BLEEDING INSIDE.

MMM...

I DIDN'T INTEND FOR YOU TO BE WOUNDED SO DEEPLY.

JUST ENOUGH TO BRING YOU HERE.

QUINTON DID THE REST.

HE TOLD YOU THE WRONG WAY TO PULL ARROWS...

AND HE TOLD THE DRAGON YOU WEREN'T REALLY A PRINCE LIKE I DRESSED YOU...

—AND THE WALL... AND HEATH...
—AND I DON'T KNOW WHAT ELSE...

I HOPE HE KNOWS WHAT HE'S DOING...

YOU CAN GO BACK.

YOU CAN ANY TIME. THIEVES ARE ALLOWED.

BUT I'M STUCK.

AND I'M...

I DON'T KNOW.

RRRRRR!

DAMN.

YES, WELL...

THAT'S ALL JUST STUPID.

THERE'RE OTHER REASONS TOO.

REAL ONES.

THERE'RE LOTS OF OTHER REASONS WE SHOULD HELP EACH OTHER.

LIKE THAT GIRL IN THE CAVE.

SHE ALMOST DID SOMETHING UNSPEAKABLE.

EVEN QUINTON KNOWS BETTER.

HE KNEW I WOULDN'T FIGHT HER. —I THINK HE WAS JUST HELPING HER TO SEE.
—GIVING HER WHAT SHE'D NEED IN ORDER TO FACE ME WHEN I DO... FOR WHEN I DID SHOW UP IN HER LIFE.

I ALWAYS WONDERED HOW SHE COULD BE SO STRONG.

QUINTON'S NOT A PERSON, RUBEL.

HE'S A FORCE OF NATURE.

REMEMBER THAT..!

BUT DON'T YOU HAVE ANY FRIENDS?

OH, RUBEL, YOU'RE SO SWEET.

I DO LOVE YOU SO..

HA! HA! HU!!..

URK!

OOOooOHooOOH

HHURINN....

FUMP-OOMP

GOODNESS... SUCH PAIN..!

OH, RUBEL...

WE ARE NOT LIKE HIM.

WE ARE NOT LIKE QUINTON.

NO MATTER HOW HARD WE TRY, OR HOW STRONG WE BECOME, WE WILL ALWAYS BE MORTAL INSIDE.

THAT'S WHY IT'S SO IMPORTANT FOR US TO BE FOR EACH OTHER.

NOBODY ELSE CARES!

NOBODY. —IF WE DON'T TAKE CARE OF EACH OTHER, THEN WE'RE JUST INVITING THEM TO USE US UP AGAIN.

AND THEY WILL!

THEY ALWAYS DO.

PRINCESS KATARA, TOO.

YOU HAVE TO FIND HER. —THAT'S WHY I BROUGHT YOU HERE REALLY, I THINK; SO YOU COULD TALK TO HER FATHER.

I'M SURE HE KNOWS WHERE SHE IS.

I'M SURE OF IT...

OH.., THERE ARE SO MANY REASONS I BROUGHT YOU HERE...

SO MANY...

Chapter 10

BAM BAM BAM

THE FRONT DOOR!

GOODNESS!

IT MUST BE THEM!

WHO ELSE COULD IT BE AS LATE AS THIS?

THE BOLT-LOCK IS BY THE OVEN

IT'S LOADED.

GO WAKE UP QUINTON. QUICKLY!

PETER! OPEN UP!

HOLD ON!

HOLD ON!

WHAT'S THIS ALL ABOUT?

WHAT DO YOU THINK THIS IS, BRINGING A MOB TO MY FRONT DOOR?!

WE'RE HERE FOR THE DUTCHY, MR. JAY.

YOU KNOW WHAT THIS IS ABOUT!

—THE MAGISTRATE HAS ISSUED NEW ORDERS FOR HIS ARREST!

WE HAVE THEM HERE.

YOU CAN READ THEM IF YOU LIKE.

QUINTON'S NOT GOING ANYWHERE!

COLLIN, WHAT'S ALL THIS NONSENSE? —WHAT'S THIS GANG OF FOOLS YOU'VE BROUGHT TO MY DOOR?

LOOK ME IN THE EYE! —YOU'RE SHUFFLING YOUR FEET LIKE AN ERRAND BOY!

IT'S TRUE, PETER.

YOU'D BEST BRING HIM DOWN.

THE PROVINCIAL MAGISTRATE HAS GRANTED THE BOROUGH A SECOND TRIAL.

PAGH! THAT'S A ROTTEN LAUGH!

IT'S THAT DAMNED LOCUMIRE, UP TO HER FILTHY TRICKS AGAIN!

YOU SHOULD KNOW BETTER THAN THIS!

IT'S THE LAW, MR. JAY.

YOU CAN'T PROTECT HIM ANY LONGER.

BRING HIM OUT, OR WE'LL COME IN AND TAKE HIM.

BARGE INTO MY HOUSE?

YOU'LL DO NO SUCH THING!

EMMA! BRING MY GUN!

WE'VE A BAND OF ROGUES OUT HERE!

HEY!

HEY THERE!

STOP THAT!

AUG

THERE!

OUT THE BACK WAY! THE DUTCHY'S ESCAPING!

ESCAPING?!

HA!

NOT I!

QUINTON, NO!

YOU HAVE TO RUN! —LIKE WE PLANNED!

FEAR NOT, GOOD LADY!

THINGS ARE MOVING MORE QUICKLY THAN I ANTICIPATED, BUT I'LL SET THIS MATTER STRAIGHT!

SO, YOU SCURVY DOGS HAVE SCRATCHED TOGETHER THE COURAGE TO COME FOR ME AT LAST, HAVE YOU?

HA!

LOCUMIRE MUST BE GETTING NERVOUS!

AND WITH GOOD REASON!

IT WILL TAKE MORE THAN ARRESTING ME TO SAVE HER NECK! SHE'S IN FAR DEEPER THAN SHE THINKS!

DON'T WORRY, HEATH.

THEY'RE GOING TO PUT ME IN JAIL, BUT I AM IN NO IMMEDIATE DANGER.

THESE ROGUES ARE USING THE LAW AS THEIR WEAPON.

THEY NEED THE ILLUSION OF **JUSTICE** BEFORE THEY CAN KILL A MAN.

THEY WON'T BE STRINGING ME UP WITHOUT SOME FARCE OF COURT ROOM THEATER FIRST.

DON'T WORRY.

- THERE WILL BE PLENTY OF TIME TO SET THINGS STRAIGHT.

SO YOU SAY **DUTCHY**.

I THINK YOU'RE THE ONE WHO'S IN DEEPER THAN YOU THINK!

WE SHALL SEE!

COME ON! COME ON! ENOUGH OF THIS!

LET'S GO.

SLAM!

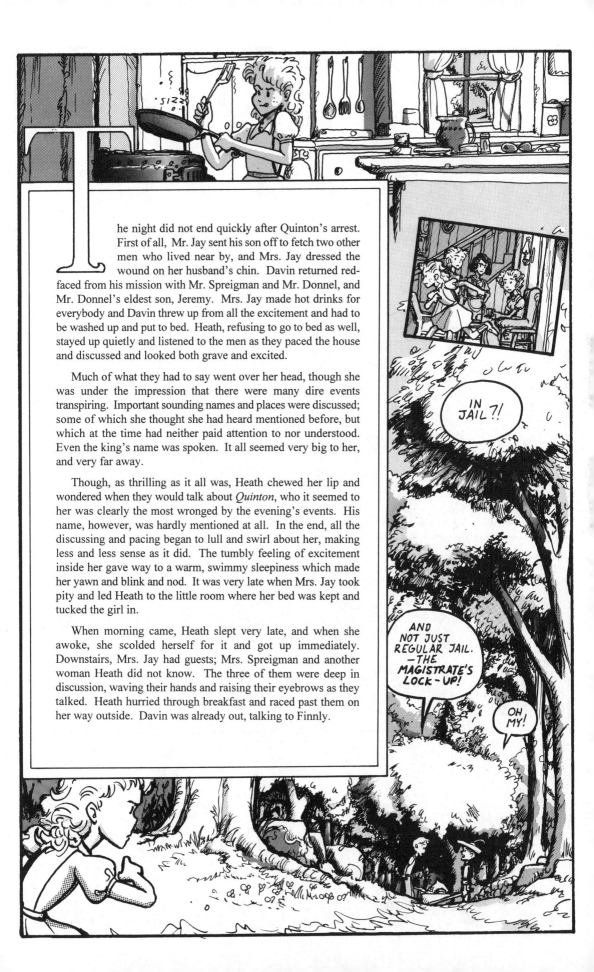

he night did not end quickly after Quinton's arrest. First of all, Mr. Jay sent his son off to fetch two other men who lived near by, and Mrs. Jay dressed the wound on her husband's chin. Davin returned red-faced from his mission with Mr. Spreigman and Mr. Donnel, and Mr. Donnel's eldest son, Jeremy. Mrs. Jay made hot drinks for everybody and Davin threw up from all the excitement and had to be washed up and put to bed. Heath, refusing to go to bed as well, stayed up quietly and listened to the men as they paced the house and discussed and looked both grave and excited.

Much of what they had to say went over her head, though she was under the impression that there were many dire events transpiring. Important sounding names and places were discussed; some of which she thought she had heard mentioned before, but which at the time had neither paid attention to nor understood. Even the king's name was spoken. It all seemed very big to her, and very far away.

Though, as thrilling as it all was, Heath chewed her lip and wondered when they would talk about *Quinton*, who it seemed to her was clearly the most wronged by the evening's events. His name, however, was hardly mentioned at all. In the end, all the discussing and pacing began to lull and swirl about her, making less and less sense as it did. The tumbly feeling of excitement inside her gave way to a warm, swimmy sleepiness which made her yawn and blink and nod. It was very late when Mrs. Jay took pity and led Heath to the little room where her bed was kept and tucked the girl in.

When morning came, Heath slept very late, and when she awoke, she scolded herself for it and got up immediately. Downstairs, Mrs. Jay had guests; Mrs. Spreigman and another woman Heath did not know. The three of them were deep in discussion, waving their hands and raising their eyebrows as they talked. Heath hurried through breakfast and raced past them on her way outside. Davin was already out, talking to Finnly.

ANYTHING ELSE! ANYTHING ELSE!

FLAP FLIP

IT'S A BIRD.

WAS IT TALKING?!

WOW.

MESSAGE! MESSAGE!

MESSAGE FOR MONSTER SLAYERS!

MESSAGE FOR HEATH!

IT'S FROM **QUINTON!!**

IT'S A MAGIC BIRD!!

IT'S A TUFTED FINCH. — FINCHES CAN'T TALK!

IT'S MAGIC! IT'S REAL MAGIC!

QUIET! LET IT TALK!

HOLD ON! I'M GONNA GET A BAG!

THERE'S A MESSAGE? FROM QUINTON?

HURRY! HURRY! RIGHT AWAY! TALK THROUGH THE BARS! FLY! FLY! GO FIND HEATH! NOT A MOMENT TO LOSE!

THROUGH THE BARS OF THE LOCK-UP?

IS SOMETHING WRONG?

HURRY, HURRY! THROUGH THE BARS! LOCKED UP TIGHT! BUT CAREFUL CAREFUL!

WATCH OUT!

FOR THE BAILIFF?

FOR THE MAGISTRATE?

WATCH OUT! NO! NO! WATCH OUT! NOT JUST MEN!

NOT JUST WITCHES! WALKS AMONG US!!

WALKS AMONG US?

WHAT DOES?

HMM..?

WHY SHOULD YOU WANT TO KNOW? IT'S NONE OF YOUR BUSINESS.

AND ANYWAY, WHO SAID YOU COULD GO ON OUR PROPERTY?

EVERYTHING ON THAT SIDE OF THE FENCE IS OURS.

PROPERTY? HUM!

FENCES...

THE LAND WAS HERE A LONG TIME BEFORE **YOU** EVER CAME ABOUT.

YOU THINK THAT PUTTING UP A FENCE OR TWO WILL MAKE THE LAND YOUR OWN?

NO.

YOU ONLY PUT UP FENCES TO SHOW THE BOUNDARIES OF YOUR **WORK**.

OF YOUR RESPONSIBILITY.

WE TREAT OUR LAND WELL. --WITH **RESPECT**. IT TREATS US WELL IN RETURN!

NOW BE GONE WITH YOU! THE THINGS YOU SEE HERE ARE NONE OF YOUR AFFAIR!

FILTHY LITTLE MUD CLERIC!

YOU DON'T KNOW A **THING**!

SHE'S A WITCH, HEATH!

I KNOW.

A WITCH?

WITCHES ALL AROUND YOU, DANGER BOY!

ALL AROUND.

MAYBE EVEN YOUR MOM, AND YOU DON'T KNOW!

MRS. JAY IS **NOT** A WITCH! --DON'T LISTEN TO HER, DAVIN!

Chapter 11

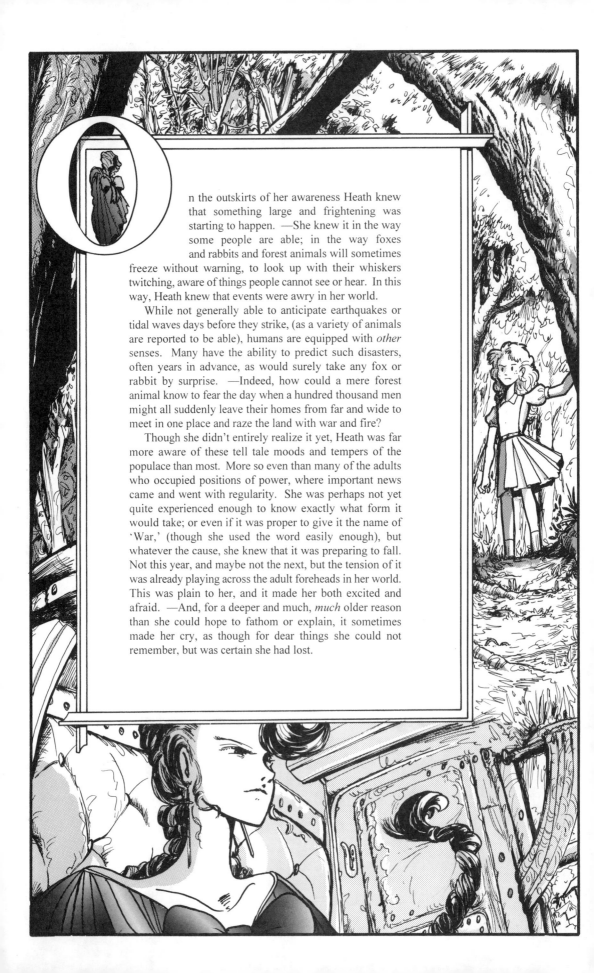

O n the outskirts of her awareness Heath knew that something large and frightening was starting to happen. —She knew it in the way some people are able; in the way foxes and rabbits and forest animals will sometimes freeze without warning, to look up with their whiskers twitching, aware of things people cannot see or hear. In this way, Heath knew that events were awry in her world.

While not generally able to anticipate earthquakes or tidal waves days before they strike, (as a variety of animals are reported to be able), humans are equipped with *other* senses. Many have the ability to predict such disasters, often years in advance, as would surely take any fox or rabbit by surprise. —Indeed, how could a mere forest animal know to fear the day when a hundred thousand men might all suddenly leave their homes from far and wide to meet in one place and raze the land with war and fire?

Though she didn't entirely realize it yet, Heath was far more aware of these tell tale moods and tempers of the populace than most. More so even than many of the adults who occupied positions of power, where important news came and went with regularity. She was perhaps not yet quite experienced enough to know exactly what form it would take; or even if it was proper to give it the name of 'War,' (though she used the word easily enough), but whatever the cause, she knew that it was preparing to fall. Not this year, and maybe not the next, but the tension of it was already playing across the adult foreheads in her world. This was plain to her, and it made her both excited and afraid. —And, for a deeper and much, *much* older reason than she could hope to fathom or explain, it sometimes made her cry, as though for dear things she could not remember, but was certain she had lost.

Heath's own private war, though, *that* was just around the corner. And this didn't require any special foresight. Not when you had magical talking birds relaying urgent messages to you, and taunting witches who knew your name and business without you knowing how. Indeed, Heath felt that if she *had* whiskers, they might well be twitching like a rabbit's.

Or a fox's.

Far in the back of her mind, where she kept those unquenchable little coals of belief which make people what they are, Heath perceived that she was somehow more special than others; that she might in fact be sharp and dangerous, like a fox. —She would never say such a thing out loud (overconfidence and conceit and other ugly traits often sprung from such feelings if one was not careful), but it didn't change the matter. And strangely, even though the feeling was very small and very private, she felt that Quinton *also* perceived those same things about her and believed in them just as much as she did.

And so, she would have marched into town all by herself to see him if necessary. —To speak through the bars of the magistrate's lock-up, as the bird had managed to instruct just before Davin frightened it away. (Were she not so preoccupied right now, she would certainly still be fuming at her cousin for doing that.)

Davin really did only have the best intentions at heart, but though Heath was strong and noble and smart, forgiveness was not her best suit. Indeed, she was as apt as the next person, if not more so, to be mean and spiteful once her anger was inspired.

But the bird had flown and the witch had spoken, and Heath was going to town with half the information and twice the anxiety she needed. (An excellent recipe for panic and disaster.)

L uckily, she did not have to go alone. Quinton had seen to that. He had, after a fashion, provided her with companions who, as simple and unwilling as they perhaps sometimes were, would nonetheless be her knights. And though they didn't know it, Davin and Finnly were perhaps better able to serve her than anybody else in the world right then. In that time and place. They knew what she knew, and they believed without hesitation, and they both loved her very much. Often it is these intangible elements of a band which can make every difference in a fight.

Unfortunately, when Jurid struck, the difference was not quite enough.

Heath was too far up the path, leading her headstrong march, and Davin was too busy trying to quiet Finnly's concerns about the wheelbarrow of gardening tools (which Finnly did not want to take with him all the way into town). And so from the darkness of an old and rotted owl's nest, the Shadow flitted down, and unfolding itself, swooped upon the girl, intending to carry her away. —And perhaps bite off her hands and feet for good measure, so that she wouldn't be able to struggle and run if she found the chance.

But Heath had whiskers that day, and catching a flicker of movement from the corner of her eye, yelped and darted just in time. With its prey startled and run beyond its reach, the apparition let out a chilling howl and flew after her through the woods, leaving a startled Finnly and Davin gaping after them.

Into the woods the shadow chased the girl, Heath scurrying through bush and bracken as quickly as her legs would carry her. Jurid swept after her like a storm, casting up dead leaves and crumbs of earth as it came. But Heath was quick and nimble like a thief, and the woods were friendly and bright. —And the shadow was nowhere nearly as strong as it had been in ages past; when it could swallow entire armies with its hate. In this day and age, it had to struggle just to stand in defiance of the morning sunlight. But even so, it could hunt a child.

From shadow to shadow it bled, hating her with a passion Heath could feel blazing upon her back like a roaring oven's heat. It would mean her end for sure if she were to but miss a step and trip. —And that was bound to happen if she did not get away soon. Nobody could run flat out for very long; not even a wily, whiskered Heath. And Jurid knew this. Jurid had chased down countless victims before her, and it *knew*, and howled after her, filled with savage glee. Though, just as Heath's breath began to give away, she and the monster burst from the bushes and into a clearing.

There, before them both, hanging from a tall tree, was a rope. *The* rope. The sort meant for pulling.

Beneath it was a large pile of dirt, recently dug, and a scattering of objects; a chair and a bottle and some other assorted things. Heath's heart leapt.

It was Quinton's trap.

But how did it work. . ? Had it even been finished? She'd not been paying close enough attention yesterday. —She'd been fighting with William Furloff. She'd barely even *looked* at what Quinton had been doing. All she remembered were ropes and pulleys. And a ladder. And an anvil.

And an enormous wine press bucket which looked as though it were intended to be hung from a tree. . .

She frantically searched the branches above, nearly tripping as she dodged from Jurid's grasp. Again she caught her breath. The wine press bucket was there, suspended high up amongst the leaves. The authorities had not yet cut it down to return it to its rightful owner. Heath wondered if the authorities even knew. William Furloff had said he would tell, except. . .

There was no time to think.

Jurid flew at her and she leaped for the rope, seeing too late that beside the new pile of earth was a recently excavated hole to match it. With a stunned gasp, Heath recalculated her jump mid-stride, and tumbled awkwardly to the ground on the far side of the pit, failing entirely to catch the rope. Jurid roared and thundered after her. Heath leaped away by barely a hair.

ow, normally, one would think that an ancient beast would have wizened over the course of many centuries to the workings of traps and trickery. Indeed, Jurid had been caught and trapped once before, inside a champagne bottle, so it knew to hate bottles and to hate the horrible thief who had done it. (The very thief McGi, in fact.)

On that occasion, Jurid had been taken entirely by surprise, snatched from the air itself and stuffed into the bottle in a rude and sudden manner. It was the first and only time Jurid had ever been seized. —And by nothing more than a man's bare hand, with not even the question of a struggle or a fight! Jurid learned then, as had many a beast and monster, to do as it was told when the thief McGi told it, and to never go back to the land of Nove again. Not ever.

But that had been long ago. The hated McGi did not roam the hills and ways of *this* land and Jurid was an apparition of shadow and smoke, able to slip through the tiniest of cracks and strike terror into the hearts of the mightiest of men. Thus with lost battles of old absent from memory, and new battles ripe to be won, Jurid's confidence swelled to bursting and all the traps and trickery of the world faded from its concern. It paid no heed to the peculiar arrangement of ropes and pulleys strung into the tree around which it chased the girl. Jurid was aware of but one thing, its mind drunk with hate, lusting only to pounce upon the young sorceress most despised, and wrest her to her doom for all that she had done. How it hated her! How it hated Heath!

And so, on the third trip around the tree, and the third jump over that treacherous pit (which having not been properly completed, really served no purpose other than to complicate matters), Heath succeeded at last in catching the rope from swinging its lazy circles in the air. Thus the trap was sprung.

PANT

DID IT GET OUT?

PANT PANT

I DON'T THINK SO.

IT'S NOT AFTER US.

WILL IT GET OUT, DO YOU THINK?

FINNLY?

I DON'T KNOW. QUINTON SAID THE BUCKET WOULD HOLD IT FOR A WHILE. BUT ONLY A BOTTLE CAN CONTAIN IT PROPERLY.

A BOTTLE?

WE BROUGHT A FEW.

THE TRAP WAS SUPPOSED TO MAKE IT SO THAT IT ENDED UP IN A BOTTLE.

HOW IN THE WORLD WAS IT GOING TO DO THAT?

WE DIDN'T FINISH DIGGING ALL THE HOLES.

THERE WERE SUPPOSED TO BE A COUPLE OF TRAP DOORS, —AND AN 'X' MARKS THE SPOT, EXCEPT WE DIDN'T FINISH.

IT'S ALL VERY COMPLICATED, BUT QUINTON WAS SURE IT WOULD WORK.

IT MADE SENSE WHEN HE EXPLAINED.

YEAH. QUINTON'S LIKE THAT.

BUT HOW WAS IT SUPPOSED TO END UP IN A BOTTLE?

WELL... IT WAS SUPPOSED TO GET SO MAD, BEING TRAPPED AND ALL, THAT IT WOULD SQUEEZE OUT THROUGH THE SPIGOT TO TRY AND GET US.

AND WHEN IT DID, WE'D CATCH IT IN A BOTTLE.

I WAS SUPPOSED TO HOLD THE BOTTLE.

I WASN'T SURE I WANTED TO, BUT QUINTON SAID IT WOULD BE OKAY.

—JUST TO HOLD IT STEADY AND STAND BRAVE.

AND THEN WE'D JUST STOPPER IT UP.

WITH A GLASS STOPPER AND WIRE.

AND THEN IT'D BE CAUGHT.

TO BE HONEST, I DIDN'T REALLY BELIEVE THAT THE MONSTER WOULD EVEN COME TO THE WOODS.

EVEN QUINTON SAID IT WAS JUST A PRECAUTIONARY MEASURE.

THIS IS ALL VERY DISTURBING.

SO, SHOULD WE DO IT, DO YOU THINK?

SHOULD WE TRY TO GET IT IN THE BOTTLE?

OF COURSE WE SHOULD! WE **HAVE** TO!

WE CAN'T HAVE THAT THING GETTING OUT AND ROAMING AROUND KILLING PEOPLE. --I WAS LUCKY JUST TO SURVIVE!

THERE'S NO WAY I COULD PULL THAT BUCKET THING OFF TWICE!

COME ON!

WELL? COME ON.

OKAY.

WE HAVE TO KICK THE SIDES OF THE BUCKET TO MAKE IT MAD, AND I'LL CATCH IT IN THE BOTTLE WHEN IT COMES OUT THE TAP.

BUT DON'T SAY ANYTHING ABOUT WHAT WE'RE DOING WHILE WE'RE OUT THERE, OR IT MIGHT GUESS WHAT WE'RE UP TO.

WE'RE LUCKY IT'S SO WEAK. --IF IT WASN'T, IT'D BE ABLE TO USE ITS SWORDS!

IT HAS _SWORDS?_

YEP. BIG ONES.

IT CAN KILL HORSES WITH ONE SLASH.

IT USED TO FIGHT DRAGONS.

HOW DO YOU KNOW?

I JUST DO.

WHERE'S THE STOPPER?

HERE, --I'VE STILL GOT IT.

ARE YOU SURE ABOUT THIS?

YES.

COME ON.

I'M GOING TO YELL. --YOU HAVE TO PRETEND TO BE HAPPY WE CAUGHT IT. --AS IF WE PLANNED IT ALL ALONG.

TONK TONK

HA HA!

WE CAUGHT IT!

WHAT A STUPID MONSTER!

AND THOSE WITCHES THOUGHT THEY HAD A CHANCE AGAINST US!

THE MONSTER SLAYERS WILL DEFEAT THEM FOR SURE!

HA!

YEAH! FOR SURE!

ERG.

RUMBLE

THIS TRAP WILL HOLD YOU FOR A **MILLION** YEARS! QUINTON BUILT IT HIMSELF!

AND THEN WE'RE GOING TO CATCH THE REST OF YOUR STUPID LITTLE WITCH ARMY, AND FINISH THEM OFF AS WELL!

SUCH MATTERS DO NOT CONCERN **US**!

THE HOLDEN LORD WALLOWS FOREVER IN HIS OWN MADNESS! HIS WORKS SHALL **FALL**! HIS LORD AND MASTER SHALL RISE FROM THE FIRES TO WHICH HE WAS CAST TO REIGN **FOREVER** THE WORLDS THREE!

RELEASE THE SHADOW!!

YESSS! RELEASE! WILL **GET** LITTLE SORCERESSS! RELEASE **ME**!!

WHO'S TALKING? HOW MANY ARE IN THERE?

HEATH?

SHH!

YEAH.

WHATEVER.

IT DOESN'T CHANGE THAT WE'VE STILL GOT YOUR STUPID JURIO!

AND IF HE'S SUPPOSED TO BE THE GREAT DAWN-SWALLOWER, THEN I'VE GOT TO LAUGH!

--NOT MUCH OF A **SHADOW MONSTER** IF YOU CAN CATCH HIM UNDER A BUCKET, **I** SAY!

I DON'T SEE HOW ANYBODY IS GOING TO RISE UP AND REIGN OVER ANY-BODY IF **THIS** IS THE BEST YOU CAN THROW AT US!

BUMP BUMP WHISHHH

WHOOSH!

CREAK! CRACK!

LO! BUT THIS CAGE IS MADE FROM FEEBLE **WOOD** AND **PINS,** AND **I** AM SHADOW AND SMOKE!

SOON THE WINDS AND RAINS WILL OPEN CRACKS AND **I SHALL BE FREE!!**

YEAH, WELL, THAT'S NOT GOING TO HAPPEN TODAY, BUDDY, SO WE'RE LEAVING NOW.

SEE YA, MISTER **SHADOW** AND **SMOKE!**

TOO BAD YOU CAN'T GET OUT AND STOP US FROM FINISHING OFF YOUR EVIL WITCH FRIENDS!

OOPS, HEY, MY **SKIRT'S** CAUGHT ON SOMETHING.

WHAT'S THIS..? SOME KIND OF **TAP?**

SQUEEE

WILL GET! WILL GET!

GROWL!

HISSS

WHICH WAY IS IT, FINNLY?

WHERE IS THE LOCK-UP?

IT'S OVER HERE, I THINK.

COME ON.

HOW WOULD YOU KNOW, HEATH?

I'VE BEEN TO TOWN BEFORE.

I THINK IT'S OVER HERE...

...

?

WHAT IS IT, HEATH?

SHH!

IT'S LADY LOCUMIRE! LOOK!

AND SHE'S MEETING SOMEBODY!

SOME GIRLS.

AND WHO'S THAT?

WHAT IS IT?

SHE IS HERE.

WHAT? THAT GIRL?

IN TOWN?

BUT I RECEIVED WORD.

I SENT JURIO AFTER HER.

THAT WAS THIS MORNING. --SURELY SHE IS CAPTURED OR SHE IS DEAD!

SHE IS NEITHER. SHE HAS DEFEATED JURIO. SHE HOLDS THE SHADOW PRISONER.

WHAT?

IT CANNOT BE! --SHE IS JUST A GIRL.

SURELY IT IS NOT POSSIBLE. --QUINTON IS MANIPULATIVE AND CRAFTY, BUT HE HAS NOT A SPARK OF MAGIC IN HIM. NO MERE GIRL COULD STOP JURIO. --I DON'T CARE WHAT HE HAS TAUGHT HER!

SHE IS NO MERE GIRL.

NO VACANCY

SHE IS MY SISTER.

YOUR SISTER?!

IT IS FOR THIS REASON YOU WERE INSTRUCTED TO WAKE ME.

I HAD NO IDEA!

I WAS TOLO QUINTON HAD A SORCERESS, BUT I HAD NO IDEA!

WHY WAS I NOT TOLO OF THIS?!

I HAVE BEEN SLEEPING FOR MORE YEARS THAN THIS AGE APPEARS ABLE TO REMEMBER.

I NO LONGER KNOW MY MASTER'S MIND.

PERHAPS HE DOES NOT TRUST YOU.

WHAT DO YOU MEAN?

I CAN SEE CLEARLY THE VISAGE OF DEPENDANCE AND HUNGER HANGING ABOUT YOU LIKE A ROT.

I SUSPECT YOU WOULD HAVE MADE FOOLISH DECISIONS IF YOU WERE GIVEN MORE KNOWLEDGE.

SHE IS IMMORTAL, THEN?

LIKE YOU?

NO.

NOT LIKE ME.

SHE CAN BE SLAIN.

SHE HAS BEEN MANY TIMES.

BUT IF IT IS TO BE DONE PERMANENTLY, IT MUST BE AT MY HAND. --ALLOWING JURID TO HUNT HER WAS AN ERROR. THE SHADOW IS A POOR TOOL WHEN IT WANTS FOR ITS TRUE MISTRESS'S HAND.

BUT I AM JURID'S MISTRESS!

THIS AFFAIR IS BEYOND YOUR SCOPE.

WHERE IS THE WIZARD KEPT?

I AM TOLD YOU WERE INSTRUCTED TO TAKE HIM PRISONER.

YES.

EXCELLENT.

YOU WILL TAKE ME TO HIM.

IF MY SISTER HAS BEEN EXPOSED TO THE SHADOW, SHE WILL SEEK OUT HER MENTOR.

I WISH TO BE THERE WHEN SHE DOES!

Chapter 12

WE'D KNOW IF SHE HAD DONE.

BUT I'M SURE SHE KNOWS YOU'RE HERE...

YES I WAS EXPECTING HER.

I HID HER TOMB AS BEST I COULD, BUT IT WAS ONLY A MATTER OF TIME BEFORE THEY FOUND HER.

I WONDER IF SHE ALSO FOUND THE MINISTER'S ALLUDICATOR.

DID SHE HAVE A BIG ROUND BOTTLE FILLED WITH BLACK SMOKE?

I DIDN'T SEE ONE

BUT IT WAS THE SAME LADY I SAW WHEN I WAS DREAMING..!

I DREAMED ABOUT HER YESTERDAY WHEN I WAS LOOKING FOR YOU!

I NEVER GOT A CHANCE TO TELL YOU THAT!

YOU CAME HOME WAY AFTER I HAD TO GO TO BED, AND I DIDN'T HAVE A CHANCE TO SEE YOU.

SO MANY THINGS HAVE HAPPENED!

YOW! --THAT'S RIGHT!

YOU DREAMED UNDER THE TREE!

WOW, YEAH. I ALMOST FORGOT ABOUT THAT!

IT'S BEEN SO LONG!

I HAD TO PLANT THAT TREE SPECIAL.

YOU PLANTED THE TREE I FELL ASLEEP UNDER?

ZZZZ

YEAH. SPECIAL DREAM TREE.

VERY DIFFICULT TIMING...

IT'S SUPPOSED TO BEAR DREAM-FRUIT EVERY SEVEN YEARS TO THE DAY.

--BUT THOSE ISLAND DRUIDS CAN BE SO UNRELIABLE.

--AND GETTING THE SEEDS FROM THEM WAS REALLY AWKWARD.

HM. I HOPE THEIR PONTIFF SURVIVED THE INSURRECTION.

NICE FELLOW.

--HE JUST HAS TROUBLE GRASPING THE IMPORTANCE OF THINGS SOMETIMES.

ANYWAY, WHAT WAS SHE LIKE?

WAS SHE A LITTLE MORE FRIENDLY THAN SHE IS NOW?

I DON'T KNOW... I THINK SO.

WE ALMOST FOUGHT, BUT SHE WOULDN'T LET US START.

THERE WERE GHOSTS AND A GIANT CAT MONSTER AND THEY WERE ALL EXPECTING US TO FIGHT, BUT SHE STOPPED IT ALL.

YES, I WAS A LITTLE WORRIED.

BUT THAT'S VERY GOOD!

DID SHE HAVE ANYBODY WITH HER?

SHE WAS SUPPOSED TO.

WAS THERE ANYBODY AT HER SIDE?

THERE WAS A BOY.

AHH! AND DID HE HAVE THE LOOK OF NOBILITY IN HIS FACE?

YES.

HE DID.

AHH..! VERA DID NOT FAIL ME.

I KNEW SHE WOULDN'T!

I WONDER WHAT HIS NAME WILL BE.

SHE CALLED HIM RUBEL.

RUBEL! THAT'S RIGHT!

THAT'S THE NAME WE AGREED UPON.

I KEEP FORGETTING.

RUBEL!

A FINE NAME! RARE.

THAT'S THE BOY YOU'RE GOING TO HAVE TO FIND.

I'M SUPPOSED TO FIND HIM?

YES. IF THINGS GO AS I SUSPECT THEY MIGHT, HE AND YOU SHOULD FIND YOURSELVES DRAWN TO EACH-OTHER.

HE IS YOUR PALADIN.

HE WILL KNOW YOU.

BUT YOU'LL HAVE TO WATCH OUT.

YOU'LL HAVE A DOUBLE WHERE YOU'RE GOING. THERE WILL BE TWO OF YOU.

AND SHE WILL ALSO CLAIM HIM AS HER OWN.

A DOUBLE?

YES. IT MIGHT BE A TOUCH DIFFICULT.

YOU MIGHT GO MAD, THERE BEING TWO OF YOU, AND ALL, SO YOU'LL HAVE TO BE CAREFUL.

WHAT DO YOU MEAN?

TWO OF ME?

I'M GOING SOMEWHERE?

YES. IT'S NOT SAFE FOR YOU HERE ANYMORE.

--WHAT WITH SALLY UP AND ABOUT.

SALLY?

WHAT ARE YOU TALKING ABOUT?

BUT I DON'T UNDERSTAND.

I'VE ONLY BEEN HERE TWO YEARS.

AND AUNT EMMA SAYS IT'S OKAY TO CALL HER 'MOM'.

I KEEP ON GETTING MOVED AROUND, AND I JUST... HRK

I KNOW...

SOB

BUT THERE ISN'T ENOUGH TIME.

YOU SEE THAT RAIN BARREL?

SNIFF UH HUH.

THAT'S THE GATE. --IT'LL TAKE YOU THERE... TO A GARDEN.

NO BOTTOM?

IT SHOULD BE QUITE SIMPLE FOR YOU. YOU JUST HAVE TO GET IN AND SWIM DOWN. THERE'S NO BOTTOM IN THE BARREL. IT JUST GOES DOWN AND DOWN.

NOT FOR YOU. HOLD YOUR BREATH AND SWIM DOWN AND DOWN, AND THEN HALF WAY THERE, YOU'LL FIND YOURSELF SWIMMING UP INSTEAD. --SO IT'S BETTER IF YOU GO IN HEAD-FIRST.

AND YOU HAVE TO SWIM WITH YOUR EYES OPEN SO YOU CAN SEE THE LIGHT AT THE OTHER END.

GO ONLY TOWARDS THE WHITE LIGHT.

THERE ARE OTHER PLACES YOU CAN GO DOWN THERE, AND I DON'T WANT YOU GOING TO ANY OF THEM.

--JUST SWIM TO THE CLOSEST OPENING.

IT'LL BE THE BRIGHTEST.

CAN YOU KEEP YOUR EYES OPEN UNDER WATER?

YES. BUT I'M NOT A VERY GOOD SWIMMER.

THAT'S OKAY

ALL YOU HAVE TO DO IS HOLD YOUR BREATH AND DOG PADDLE THROUGH THE WATER.

IT'S JUST THE GOING IN HEAD-FIRST THAT'S THE HARD PART.

MM...

IT'S BEST IF YOU GO NOW.

YOUR SISTER WILL BE COMING SOON.

MY SISTER?

--THE LADY YOU SAW.

THE LADY IN BLACK.

YOU SHOULD HAVE GUESSED THAT ALMOST RIGHT AWAY.

BUT I DON'T HAVE A SISTER.

HOW COULD I HAVE A SISTER?

MY PARENTS NEVER SAID.

IT'S NOT EASY TO EXPLAIN.

YOUR PARENTS WOULDN'T HAVE KNOWN ABOUT HER. SHE WAS BORN A LONG, LONG TIME AGO. --LONG BEFORE THEM.

YOU WERE BORN A LONG TIME AGO TOO. YOU WERE TWINS. --BUT YOU DIED WHEN YOU WERE JUST A YOUNG WOMAN.

YOU KEEP GETTING RE-BORN AND NOW YOU'RE HERE

YOU HAVE BOTH COME A LONG WAY.

Heath looked deep, but could see nothing out of the ordinary, except that she was not at all happy about any of this. It had been fun and exciting just before she got here. It had been serious too, but somehow she believed that everything was going to be okay and that she and Davin and Finnly and Quinton were going to save the day together. Falling into this dizzy kind of thinking had been easy enough after the capture of Jurid, which really *was* a remarkable feat; far more than Heath knew or had been given credit for. Long ago, Jurid really *had* been called the Dawn Swallower, and though the beast was much weaker now, Heath by all rights should not have survived. She was very lucky.

She did not, however, have long to contemplate this because all at once, Soracia arrived.

Soracia. Sally. The Shadow Lady. Queen of Halves. Heath's dark sister. . . And the woman who would one day seek the company of a boy thief for comfort and relief, and perhaps friendship and love. All the same person, she strode down the alley-way with a countenance of ice and hatred and swirls of black magic which seemed to cause all the world to crash loose.

Heath and Soracia locked eyes, and for a moment the dark queen felt triumph pawing at her heart, knowing that Heath would be drawn into battle by forces which had grown nearly irresistible with the passing of the ages. —Especially irresistible for an inexperienced mortal child. But Heath, with an effort that made her gasp and clench her teeth, turned away and leaped toward the barrel. Soracia squinted at her sister, momentarily confused, and then realizing at once the danger, flew like a bat upon the barrel into which the girl was struggling.

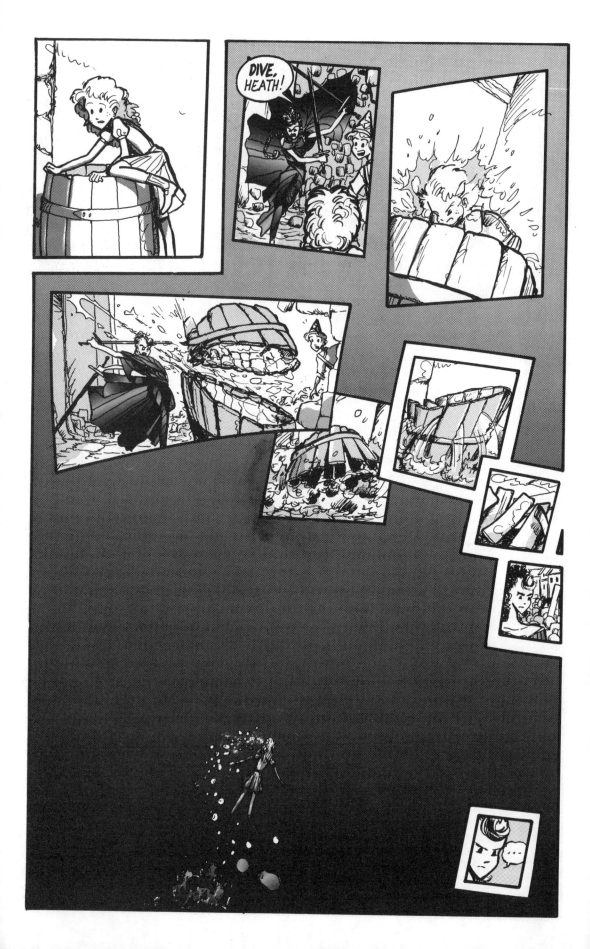

Last Page of The Story.

Well now!

What a dirty place to end a volume! With Heath clearing her eyes to gaze upon a new and misty dream world. Such a thing!

Though again, same as last time, to make up for it, I'll say a little about what you can expect in the next volume. . .

To begin with, Rubel and Heath do finally run into one another. (I've been anticipating this meeting for quite some time now.) As well, I'll be dealing with some old characters who have not been mentioned since the very first chapter of the first volume.

Varkias also comes back into the picture, (from which he's been absent for. . . Goodness! *That* long? —When you consider that every twenty pages of this book constitutes about two months of writing and cartooning, it's been quite some time for the little guy to be away).

Anyhow, as well in volume three I'll be introducing for the first time one of my favourite characters. The monster, Chead. (Who, incidentally, lives inside something I originally called the Eye Box, which I may choose to rename when the time comes). There's lots of story connected to *that* particular element.

Finally, depending on how many issues I decide the third book will reprint, princess Katara may or may not be showing up next time around. Six or Twelve issues will likely make the difference. . .

Hmm. . .

Speaking of which, I am reminded of just how much work I've still got left to do if she's going to appear at *all*. Sheesh.

Well, I must get back to it! So goodbye for now, and take care!

His eagerness he tried to slow,
working up the spiral stair,
for where he went he did not know
but knew he should take care!

The End